SPACE, TIME, AND RELATIVITY

The Einstein Universe

By H. HORTON SHELDON, PH. D.

PROFESSOR OF PHYSICS, NEW YORK UNIVERSITY

Highlights of Modern Knowledge

RELATIVITY

THE UNIVERSITY SOCIETY

INCORPORATED

NEW YORK

CONTENTS

CHAPTER   PAGE

I   RELATIVITY AND ITS AUTHOR 1

Understanding Einstein—Public Acclaim—The Man and the Scientist—Einstein's Contributions—Biographical Sketch—His Hobbies

II   THE HISTORICAL BACKGROUND FOR EINSTEIN'S THEORIES .. 15

Contributions from the Classic Period—The Renaissance —Sir Isaac Newton—The Eighteenth and Nineteenth Centuries—Quantum Theory—Interpretation of Modern Advances—The Ether

III   THE SPECIAL THEORY OF RELATIVITY 35

Location and Motion—Measurement and Position—Absolute and Relative Motion—Michelson-Morley Experiment —Velocity and Motion—The Laws that Govern Motion —Velocity and Light—Time and Space—Relativity of Length—Energy and Mass—Velocity of Light as a Proof of Einstein's Theory—Astronomical Confirmation of the Special Theory—The Special Theory and Everyday Experience

IV   THE GENERAL THEORY OF RELATIVITY 55

Force and Gravitation—The Gravitational Field—Behavior of Light in a Gravitational Field—Properties of Space —Curved Space—A Finite Universe?—Size of the Universe—The Warping of Space—Gravitational Space and Time—Perihelion Movement of the Planet Mercury—Curvature of Light in the Sun's Gravitational Field

V   EINSTEIN'S FIFTH PAPER 77

The Aim of Science—Einstein's Contribution to Unification of Phenomena—Euclidean Geometry—Non-Euclidean Geometry—The Uniform-Field Equations—Significance of New Field Equations—Solution of the Field Equations—Value of Einstein's Work—The Future

APPENDIX I 92

APPENDIX II 94

SUGGESTIONS FOR FURTHER READING 96

GLOSSARY 98

INDEX 101

SPACE, TIME, AND RELATIVITY

The Einstein Universe

By H. Horton Sheldon, Ph.D.

PROFESSOR OF PHYSICS
NEW YORK UNIVERSITY

ACKNOWLEDGMENT

IN this attempt to make clear to the layman the principles of Einstein's theories and to explain their significance the author wishes to acknowledge the invaluable assistance of his associate in the Department of Physics of New York University, Mr. Edgar N. Grisewood, without whose co-operation this book would not have been attempted.

H. Horton Sheldon

New York, 1932.

ALBERT EINSTEIN

CHAPTER I

RELATIVITY AND ITS AUTHOR

IT HAS so often been said that there are but six men in the entire world capable of understanding the theories of Einstein that I hesitate to repeat the statement here. The number of this very exclusive group sometimes is stated as high as twelve. It depends upon the teller. But it is never less than six. On this score there is at least one group the members of which according to a humorist are even more exclusive. This, he says, is the group of but four people in the entire world who have never attempted to understand Einstein.

Although you are doubtless somewhat amused at this apparent exaggeration of the universal attempt to find out what Einstein's theories are all about, it may not occur to you that the statement that there are but six men capable of understanding Einstein is an almost equal exaggeration. If one sets out to understand Einstein he will find himself on a very rough mathematical path. It is this which deters or completely blocks the path to understanding unless one wishes to spend the time and energy necessary to overcome the blockade. True, not every one is capable of success in this direction, but there are many persons gifted with sufficient mathematical ability to do so.

But a complete understanding of all the mathematical shorthand, which Einstein finds it necessary to use for rigorous proof of his theories, is not necessary if one wishes to understand the physical principles involved and the conclusions reached. It is unnecessary for the passenger who wishes to travel from one city to another by train to make the detailed survey of the ground which was made when the track was first laid out. In fact, he may have a more general conception of the whole country that is spread out before him as he travels than the surveyor obtained who measured it all off with tape and level. Such a view of Einstein is not difficult to grasp, and it is possible for any one capable of obtaining a public school education to understand the fundamental principles upon which the Einstein theories are based and to realize the significance of some of the conclusions reached. I hope that between these covers I will be able to prove the truth of this statement.

UNDERSTANDING EINSTEIN

It is quite likely that Einstein owes some of his popularity today to the very statement which I have just been discussing—to the fact that it has so often been said that but six men could understand him. It is at once a challenge to the human intelligence. Every one likes to feel that he is capable of understanding what his fellows are capable of understanding. In a matter of pure intellect one does not like to be so roughly pushed aside. Should I tell you that you have not the voice of a Caruso, that you cannot handle a bow like a Kreisler, you will accept my words without question if you are not a musician. These things depend much upon a natural aptitude which you will admit you do not possess. You do not feel disgraced if you cannot run a hundred yards in ten seconds. You are not an athlete, you will say. But let me tell you that you cannot understand what I am going to say to my friend and you feel that I have insulted your intelligence. To understand the *mathematics* of Einstein requires an ability just as special as that required by the great vocalist or by the great runner. It requires a natural aptitude in mathematics. If you haven't got it, then you will have to rest content with understanding only what it is all about. This, as I have already said, is not especially difficult.

Another reason we wish to understand Einstein is that he deals with the universe, the myriad specks of material scattered through space of which our earth forms but one. We feel that if we can reach out into space and find out more about the universe we may gain a better conception of the place our earth holds in it and of the importance which we can attach to our own existence. It is all part of that desire of man, which has existed throughout the ages, to know more of himself, where he has come from, where he is going, and what is to be the final destiny of the human race. We are ever trying to solve this gigantic mystery—a riddle more intriguing, with more clues crossing each other, more hopeless of solution, than the darkest murder tale.

Again our simple curiosity is aroused. We are told that there is no such thing as *absolute motion,* that all motion is *relative.* The notion of absolute motion is so ingrained into us, because of our childhood concepts of an earth which is at rest, that this thought seems revolutionary. We are told that we cannot measure the length of any object absolutely, that its length changes with its velocity. We are told that if we could travel with a speed greater than that of light we could catch up to and see images of things which were on this earth centuries ago. Certainly few things could arouse our interest as statements of this kind undoubtedly do. The ideas are fascinating. We are in that same condition of wonder which must have greeted the discovery that the earth was round. Yet today we accept this fact without winking an eyelash. Of course the earth is round! Perhaps a century hence Einstein's ideas will be just as readily accepted by every schoolboy.

So general has the interest in Einstein's work been that it is safe to say that never before has the work of any one scientist attracted so much attention. A mere announcement in the press that a film showing the Einstein fundamentals would be exhibited brought such crowds to the American Museum of Natural History in the city of New York that the result was described, without exaggeration, as a riot. Hundreds were turned away and other hundreds waited for a second showing. This event is still referred to as the "Einstein riot."

Public Acclaim

When Einstein presented his now famous fifth paper before the Prussian Academy of Sciences the whole paper was cabled to the New York *Herald Tribune* and was published, complicated equations and all, on the front page the next morning. Not only was the entire edition sold out, but the city was combed for copies by the newspaper itself to satisfy the mail demand. When this was found impossible, serious consideration was given to reprinting the entire paper. Telegrams and letters came

from every part of the country from other publications con-
gratulating this paper on the best bit of journalism in years.
Why was this good journalism? Not one person in every ten
thousand who rushed out to buy this paper had the slightest conception of what it was about. Yet it was news, and in the words
of one editor it is the function of the press to give the people
the news whether they can read it or not. The author, of this
book, if you will pardon the mention of it, had the honor of
deciphering the cables, and the equations as translated are shown
in Figure 1, reprinted through the courtesy of the *Herald
Tribune*.

The Man and the Scientist

It is safe to say that never before has the entire contents of
a mathematical paper been published, in full, as front-page news
in a great metropolitan newspaper. The compliment to Einstein is nothing short of colossal. Yet, looking at it from another angle, he is paid greater compliments by the press almost
daily. The fifth paper, so-called, to which reference has just
been made, marks one of the milestones of his career. It is
therefore just, if we admire the man, as we evidently do, that
it should be given the prominence that its contents warrant. It
is, however, only profound respect for the man himself which
prompts the press to give front-page notice to every utterance,
to every opinion of this sage, whether in his field of science or
not. His every thought has come to be regarded as important.
It is one thing to give him credit for advances in his chosen field
—the science of physics; it is another to strain our ears to hear
what he has to say on current affairs of politics, economics, etc.
It is quite likely true that no scientist has ever been granted so
many columns of publicity as has Einstein.

If the great scientist were to employ a whole retinue of press
agents it is doubtful if they could add more than a few lines to
the press notices which have been given him. It is indeed a
splendid example of the old mousetrap quotation.* Although
he lives in a quiet and rather obscure village in Germany, and

---

* "If a man can write a better book, preach a better sermon, or make a better
mousetrap than his neighbor, though he built his house in the woods, the world
will make a beaten path to his door."—*Generally accredited to Emerson.*

Die lokalen n-Beine sind alle "parallele" gestellt. Parallele und gleiche Vektoren sind solche, welche—auf ihr lokales n-Bein bezogen—gleiche Koordinaten haben. Die Parallelverschiebung eines Vektors wird durch die Formel

$$\delta A^M = -\Delta^M_{\alpha\beta} A^\alpha \delta x^\beta = -sh^{MS} h_{\alpha,\beta} A^\alpha \delta x^\beta$$

gegeben, wobei in

Excerpt from his "Field Theory" pamphlet as printed in German

the local N dash legs are all placed quote parallel unquote and equal vectors are such as have dash with reference to their local N dash leg undash equal cordinates stop the parallel disarrangement of a vector will given by formula delta capital a raised Mu equal to minus capital Delta raised Mu sub alpha beta endsub capital a raised alpha Mhdraise Delta X raised beta equals minus S H raised Mu S end raise H sub alpha comma beta endsub capital A raised alpha endraise Delta X raised beta whereby in raise   draise H sub alpha comma bet

The same excerpt as it reached the Herald Tribune in condensed English over the cable

Technical Feat Of Transmission Amazes Experts

Intricate Einstein Formulas Described in Words by Cable and Reconstructed

Eminent professors of mathematics and physics capable of understanding Einstein's latest contribution to the advancement of knowledge, were interested yesterday in knowing how the

perscript s h subscript v.

The local n-legs are all placed "parallel," and equal vectors are such as have—with reference to their local n-leg—equal co-ordinates.

The parallel disarrangement of a vector will be given by the formula

$$\delta A^M = -\Delta^M_{\alpha\beta} A^\alpha \delta x^\beta$$

$$= -sh^{\alpha\beta} h_{(\alpha,\beta)} A^\alpha \delta x^\beta$$

whereby in

As it appeared in the Herald Tribune decoded and with the formula in equation form

photographs. John Elliott, of the Herald Tribune Berlin Bureau, trans-lated the verbal text

Figure 1

well on the outskirts of that village, there has been worn a well-beaten track to his door. Some have said that his very manner of reticence accounts for the eagerness of reporters to get a story. There are plenty of other people who deny entrance and information to reporters, yet they are not troubled. Were they to let down the barriers they would not be robbed of every peaceful moment of the day as would this great international scientific hero. How, then, are we to account for the tremendous interest which the world has taken in Einstein?

Einstein's Contributions

First of all there can be no question as to the motive which prompts scientists to interest themselves in Einstein. It is his great genius in things scientific. He has changed the whole mode of scientific thought. His contributions are not alone on relativity. If all the mathematical work he has done in this particular field were to be wiped aside he would still remain one of our greatest physicists. His contributions to the field of electronic, atomic, and molecular physics are tremendous. He was able to build up an equation to test the theory of Brownian movements * in gases which had puzzled physicists for more than fifty years. This was in 1905. Never-ceasing (or rapid) zigzag movements of smoke particles, larger than molecules but so small that they can only be seen under a high-power microscope, were such as to suggest life. In fact, many years before, the responsibility for this motion, as seen in the motion of colloidal particles in suspension, was attributed to life. Einstein was able to show, through calculations, later checked by experiment by others, that the motions were due to unequal bombardment of molecules on the two sides of the particle. This is the strongest proof of the *kinetic theory,* the theory which tells us that all matter is made up of molecules which are in motion.

Again, Einstein made a fundamental contribution to the study of photo-electricity, the science which underlies the photo-electric cell. Light falling on suitable surfaces frees electrons which carry the current in an electric circuit. Thus light

---

* So called after Robert Brown, a British botanist, who first observed them in the sap of plants.

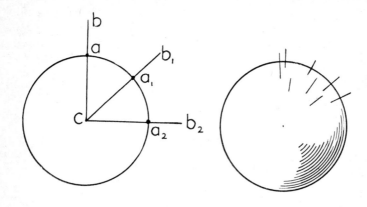

RELATIVITY OF DIRECTION

Let us consider direction—up, down, north, south, east, west. When we state that something is straight down we mean that it is located on an imaginary straight line drawn from a given point to the center of the earth; when we state that something is straight up, we mean that it is located on an outward extension of the straight line connecting the given point with the center of the earth. For example let a, a_1, a_2 be given points on the surface of the earth; any point on the lines ac, a_1c, a_2c is straight down from these given points, and any point on the lines ab, a_1b_1, a_2b_2 is straight up from these points. It is interesting to note that the path of a balloon ascending from a_2 to b_2 is at right angles to the path of a balloon ascending from a to b. Up or down from any one point on the earth's surface has a unique direction—we might say a private direction of its own differing from that of every other point on the earth's surface. Within the gravitational field of the earth, "up" or "down" has no meaning except relative to some given point within that field.

Should we be able to send a rocket from the earth to the moon the moment it left the gravitational field of the earth and entered the gravitational field of the moon, or to be more exact, when the gravitational pull of the moon became greater than that of the earth, "up" and "down" to the rocket would be in reference to the center of the moon's mass. Could we place ourselves in outer space free from any gravitational field, "up" and "down" would be meaningless. The same is true of "north," "south," "east," and "west"; in outer space these directions have no meaning. Even at two points on the earth's surface three of these four directions lose their meaning—there is no "north," "east," or "west" at the north pole, and no "south," "east," or "west" at the south pole.

Therefore we see that *direction* is relative.

7

changes are converted into electric changes. It is this principle that has given us such a flood of robots. His famous photo-electric cell equation gave us the exact relation between the nature of the light striking the photo-electric surface and the energy of the electrons given off. And so one could go on to the other fundamental problems which Einstein has solved quite outside the field of relativity with which his name is usually connected. This is enough, however, to account for the great respect accorded him by scientists and to account for the importance which is granted by all to his views on scientific matters. It does not exactly account, however, for the respect with which he is listened to on other matters. What is the reason for this?

BIOGRAPHICAL SKETCH

We are more than ready to listen to Einstein on current affairs quite outside of his own field, because in the past his views have been both sound and eminently fair. We have only to know what kind of man he is to realize that they could not be otherwise. Let us look at his past life and his present manner of living in order that we may realize the truth of this.

When Albert Einstein was born in 1879, he was not born to a life of ease and luxury, but was the son of a Jewish merchant in Ulm. Both financial difficulty and the anti-Semitic feeling toward his race made it hard for him to advance. His teachers in Munich, where he went to school at an early age, were, to quote him, "like non-commissioned officers." At sixteen he went to Switzerland where he felt a freer atmosphere, and where, due to his own efforts, he was able to complete his training for the doctorate degree. At twenty-three he was glad to have a position as technical expert in the Swiss patent office. Since he himself had been treated somewhat unfairly in his early life, while at the same time he had to earn his own way, it is not surprising that we find him both fair and most sympathetic toward those who are today struggling upward, especially toward the young aspirant. This early treatment, no doubt, also accounts for his retiring nature. The opportunity largely lacking, he did not learn to mix freely with others in a social way in his youth.

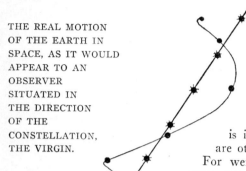

THE REAL MOTION
OF THE EARTH IN
SPACE, AS IT WOULD
APPEAR TO AN
OBSERVER
SITUATED IN
THE DIRECTION
OF THE
CONSTELLATION,
THE VIRGIN.

RELATIVITY

OF

REST AND MOTION

When we say that an object is in motion we infer that there are other objects which are at rest. For were all objects moving at the same rate we should have no way of finding it out. Since all objects on the earth move with the earth as it rotates and as it revolves about the sun, we should not know that it was moving were we unable to sight on some astronomical object to see that it was doing so. Even at that, the ancients preferred to think that the earth was stationary and that the other bodies were in motion around it.

It is impossible for us to say that any body is absolutely at rest unless we have some point of reference which we know to be absolutely at rest with respect to space. Such a point we shall never find. We can refer all motion on the earth to the earth itself and say that a body is at rest when it is not moving with respect to the earth. But we know that the earth is not only rotating on its axis but is revolving about the sun as well. The path which any point on the earth travels is a complicated, winding one. We can assume that the sun is at rest and take our measurements from that as a center. But it is not at rest. It is moving through the universe at a measurable rate. We can assume that the center of the universe is stationary and use that as our reference point. But do we know that our universe is stationary? Perhaps it too is moving through a universe of universes.

All motion, then, is relative. There is no such thing as absolute motion or rest. All our measurements must be taken with respect to some other object concerning the motion of which we may not be aware. Motion with respect to the earth is all we need to consider if we are making speed laws for motorists but such narrowness of view will not suffice for purposes of science.

Illustration is from The Pageant of the Stars *by Willem J. Luyten, and is used by the kind permission of the author and of his publishers, Doubleday, Doran & Company.*

He has made little, if any, effort to do so since—he most enjoys his own society and thoughts and is happiest when pulling on his pipe in his small study, or sailing his boat, as he does for hours at a time, on the lake which his modest home overlooks.

Einstein has learned, perhaps through necessity in his youth, to live a full life without stimulation from contact with others. He recognizes fully the work of others, but his is a life of quiet meditation. He knows not when he works. A pencil, a paper and his pipe are his tools. He is in no hurry to finish anything. He thinks things out as few people do in this day of snap judgments. Perhaps that is another reason why his judgment on nearly any matter is correct and fair.

Einstein has apparently failed to be impressed by the advertisements, which he must have seen in American magazines, which warn us that we should always keep our eyes on the job ahead. In so far as high position and wealth are concerned, Einstein has little ambition. Both high official position and wealth could be his for the asking. He has no desire for either. One might well say that so far as position is concerned he has reached that which might be the envy of any man. Yet not every one would be satisfied with the place he has reached, which, after all, is merely a place in the minds of his fellowmen. It carries with it no authority, and but little gold. It is a glory which he could, at most, sense; but which it is safe to say he greatly underestimates. This glory apparently gives him no great pleasure. Rather the contrary; it brings to him a burden of notoriety which he would gladly shake off. It is not in the man to play to the grandstand. And when he is forced into the glare of the limelight, as upon his arrival in New York late in 1930, it is a rather painful experience. Fortunately his wife tempers the shock by her easy way and graceful manner of appearing to grant every request without ever fully granting any. It is safe to say that Einstein would be much happier if he could pursue his work unknown to any one.

His Hobbies

Einstein gets his pleasure in his work with no thought of the remuneration that might come from it. It is this, again, which

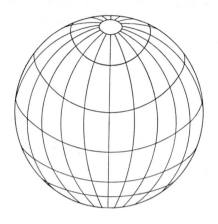

RELATIVITY OF EARTH TIME

Let us assume that it is possible to travel around the earth in twenty-four hours, and that a traveler starts from some point on the equator at noon, July 2nd, when the sun is directly overhead and travels due west. Six hours later he is a quarter of the way around the globe. At this point it is still noon July 2nd, with the sun directly overhead. Six hours more elapse and he is just about to cross the International Date Line. It is still noon July 2nd. A second later he has crossed the line. It is now noon July 3rd. When he completed three-quarters of the journey it is noon July 3rd and at noon July 3rd he arrives at the point from which he started.

This example is commonplace enough, but it serves to emphasize the fact that every point in his path had a private "noon" of its own.

Assume that the traveler makes another journey westward, starting from some point halfway between the equator and the north pole, always keeping the same distance from the pole. The distance he travels in order to return to his starting point will be considerably shorter than was the distance covered in his equatorial journey. In order to conform to local time, it is necessary for him to set his watch back six hours at each quarter point of the circle he is following. The distances between these points are miles less than they were in his journey in following the equator.

Theoretically, he could travel a circle twelve feet in circumference around the north pole; then every three feet he would have to set his watch back six hours. If he could place himself exactly at the Pole he could select any time he wished. He could step out on one meridian and it would be noon, step out on another meridian and it would be midnight.

adds weight to whatever Einstein may say. We know that the man has no ax to grind. He is never suspected of self-seeking.

No doubt the thinking process is Einstein's greatest pleasure. His is the enjoyment that comes to the creative genius. He sees his work gradually being constructed, bit by bit, and he thrills to see it grow. He must try many bits of timber before he gets one that fits. Each is tested with scientific patience. If it does not work it is discarded. When things are not going well he stops work outwardly. The mental process still goes on. Then he sees a new avenue of approach and he works feverishly from then on until a thorough test of his new idea has been made. We are told that when he is working hardest, when he is making rapid progress, his usually delightful disposition disappears. He is decidedly snappy if interrupted. This is but natural—it is the case with nearly all creative artists. They find it most annoying to have their train of thought interrupted. Some very temperamental persons will give up work for hours, or even for the day, if seriously interrupted. When Einstein is inspired, then is the time to get his thoughts on paper. Under such conditions he works with almost religious fervor. It is even said that he will develop a fever. Then it is that great things are accomplished. New conceptions of our universe are born to the world. It is almost as if, at such times, Einstein had the power to remove himself from this puny earth and to look back at it and the rest of the universe as would some colossal giant. Like many mathematicians, Einstein is also a musician. His pleasure in this hobby ranks with his pipe, his boat, and his work. In music he expresses himself through the medium of his violin, an instrument which he plays with great talent. Perhaps the concert stage was robbed that we might have a great creative thinker. He also plays the piano well, but not as well as he plays the violin. He plays the piano only when alone or with close friends.

Such is Einstein: We have tried to convey to the reader the man as we see him. We have avoided trying to analyze the most analyzed man of our time. He has been accounted for on almost every possible theory. He has been picked apart by psychologists who are interested in such facts as that he was very slow as a child. We are told that he was so slow in learning to talk that his parents despaired that he would ever talk and took him to experts for examination. In school he was very ordinary. We are told by biologists that he is a mutation or a "sport" as such types are sometimes called. He is one of those rare occurrences such as a five-legged calf or a two-headed rooster. We are told that the laws of chance will probably not produce another such mind in several hundred years. His is a genius which is not inheritable; and so on, and so on.

Such critical analyses tend to rob the man of his reality. They detract from, rather than add to, our understanding of him. Under such close scrutiny we almost forget that he is a man. Yet he is so decidedly human that he makes such statements appear rather flat. We should like to know whether they amuse or annoy him. Our guess is that he finds them mildly amusing.

In these few pages we have attempted to give such a sketch of the man as we feel that he himself would consider a truthful account, with the exception that he would deny being a genius. In this we have the preponderance of public opinion with us even though he were to object. We feel that we cannot do him complete justice in so little space. In the pages to follow, however, much will be added to what we have said if we succeed in building up an appreciation of his work. After all it is quite likely that he would prefer that our appreciation go to his work rather than to himself. We feel that we have built up a sufficient atmosphere to add somewhat to the enjoyment of what follows, to enable you, perhaps, to feel that you can see the great man at work in his study as you read. Or if you like to dream, let yourself sail with him in his boat, the fragrant smoke from his briar pipe drifting into your nostrils as he makes notes on his pad of paper, notes which many times transformed have now found their way into your hands in the form of this little book.

OUTSTANDING FACTS FROM CHAPTER I

1. It has ever been the aim of science to seek a fundamental law underlying the mysteries of all natural phenomena. This search by Einstein for a universal law has resulted in the *general* and *special* laws of relativity, the latter a special or specific application of the former.
2. To obtain a definite idea of what Einstein has accomplished in the field of relativity it is not necessary to understand the intricate mathematical shorthand appearing in the formulas.
3. Aside from relativity, Einstein's contributions to science have been many and noteworthy:
    a. Through his calculations, he was able to show that "Brownian movements" in gases were due to an unequal bombardment of molecules on the two sides of a colloidal (jelly-like) particle. This further substantiated the *kinetic theory*.
    b. He later made a fundamental contribution to the study of photo-electricity, formulating an equation giving the exact relation between the nature of the light striking the photo-electric surface and the energy of the electrons given off. An example of this is found in the photo-electric cell used for television, etc.
4. Intimate facts concerning Einstein the man:
    a. He was the son of a Jewish merchant at Ulm, Germany.
    b. He struggled against financial difficulties and also against anti-Jewish feeling, both socially and scholastically.
    c. He obtained his doctorate in Switzerland.
    d. He became a technical expert in the Swiss Patent Office.
    e. He lives apart and without stimulation from contact with others.
    f. He does not seek wealth nor high position, though both could be his for the asking.
    g. His pleasures are his work, his music, his pipe, and his boat.

CHAPTER II

THE HISTORICAL BACKGROUND FOR EINSTEIN'S THEORIES

THE English dramatist and philosopher, George Bernard Shaw, in an address referred to Einstein as one who had "discovered a new universe." But as the old adage has it, "There is nothing new under the sun," and we would expect to find at least a few speculations suggesting the existence of the "new universe" at an earlier date. Even a casual study of the history of science shows that the great discoveries have not come entirely from a clear sky—not that any less credit is due to the genius who finally establishes the "new" because others bandied with the idea without being able to fix it as a scientific truth. In this respect the development of an hypothesis and the development of a technical device, the telephone for example, are much the same. Neither idea nor device germinates and grows to full bloom in the brain of one inventor—the seed, at least, has come from elsewhere and, more than likely, some necessary watering also. Yet without a master-brain in which to take root, the seed might never bring forth fruit, no matter how much watering came its way.

Before definitely starting a search for the forerunners of Einstein's brilliant hypothesis, it will be worth our while to go down the ages and note how the conception of space and time has developed.

Contributions from the Classic Period

As far back as the fifth century before Christ we find a Greek of the Ionian School, Heraclitus, who appreciated the existence of the time element. He expressed a conception of constant change by saying, "You cannot step twice into the same river." The location may be identical but the water is always different.

About a hundred years later, in the teachings of Protagoras, the Greek Sophist, the subjective nature of man's experience with the world is stressed. "Man is the measure of all things, of what is that is, and of what is that is not." Although rather too egocentric for present-day science, this is a warning of the grave difficulty which must arise if an absolute measurement is desired.

Some hundred and fifty years passed and Epicurus, although interested in physics only as a means to an understanding of the universe as a problem in ethics, nevertheless elaborated the earlier doctrines of Democritus and greatly influenced the Latin poet Lucretius. Thus reasoned Epicurus: "Nothing is created out of nothing, and nothing passes into nothing. The universe consists in bodies and space. The existence of bodies is testified by sense and the existence of space is a necessary inference from reason; for if the void did not exist, bodies could not move as, in fact, sense assures us that they do move. Again the universe is infinite, for the finite has an extremity which can only be observed against something else, which is impossible in the case of the universe." This is probably the most concise and comprehensible view of relations between matter and space to be found in the writings of the ancients.

In Aristotle, despite the fact that until the seventeenth century he remained the prime authority in matters physical as in all other intellectual fields, we find no contribution of real value. Perhaps his reference in the *"De coelo"* to the dynamical nature of the universe might be considered as an advance over the statical view expressed by Plato; but the reasoning given is certainly quite obscure. Of all the contributions by the Greeks, with the exception of that of Archimedes, it must be said that the mind, not the laboratory, was the source. Lacking an experimental groundwork their theories represent feats of logic; remarkable in some instances, yes; but of no great importance in the development of a physical science.

Let us turn to the Roman poet Lucretius (Titus Lucretius Caius), born 96 B.C., in whose *"De rerum natura"* any physicist, chemist, or biologist of today may find at least an inkling of his own pet theory. In physics, there is little here to add to our

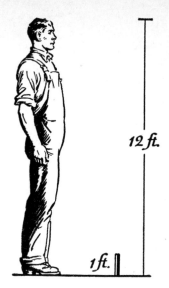

RELATIVITY OF MEASUREMENT

Suppose I buy a yard of cloth from a merchant, wash it, and take it next day to a second merchant who measures it for me and finds it less than a yard in length. Was the first merchant a scoundrel, or did the cloth shrink? If access to the first merchant's yardstick is denied me I shall never be able to tell.

Suppose it were possible, overnight, for some practical joker to shorten every measuring rule in the land. The next morning we would notice nothing unusual in the appearance of our surroundings, but if we were to measure objects, whose size we knew from previous measurements, we should find that their dimensions had increased. Our measuring rods would indicate that we were taller than we had been, that our streets were longer, our houses higher. Could we tell what had happened? Are our measuring rods smaller than they were or has everything else in the universe increased in size? We have no means of finding out. We must remain forever in ignorance as to what actually happened.

Thus all our measurements are purely relative. Our measurements are merely comparisons, one thing with another. If one changes, the relations are changed; but we do not know what has been altered.

Suppose, however, that not only did the measuring rods shorten but that everything else in the universe contracted in exactly the same ratio. Would it then be possible to detect any change? The answer to this is "No." If every object in the universe were either to expand or contract an equal amount we should have no means of detecting the change. Men might decrease in size until they were no larger than the present size of a flea; or they might become taller than a modern skyscraper. But if everything else changed in exactly the same proportion it would never be known that any change had come about.

17

collection, for it is mostly a repetition of the teachings of Epicurus. One quotation will serve as a keynote for our view; "Knowledge comes through the senses whose evidence we must accept as unimpeachable."

The scholastics of the Middle Ages contributed nothing new to the science of physics. During this period the works of Aristotle were regarded with a degree of veneration which would brook not the slightest criticism. Yet there were rebellious souls, one of whom at least merits our mention because of his boldness in advocating the experimental method—the cornerstone of modern science. This one was Roger Bacon (1214?-1294). Apparently possessed of a keen mind far in advance of his contemporaries, Bacon won only imprisonment in recognition.

THE RENAISSANCE

The Renaissance period may be regarded as the natal period of modern science. During this time we find the break from established teachings in astronomy and physics and the rise of the new type of reasoning firmly grounded in experiment. Probably it is unfair to attribute the initial step on the new pathway to any one individual, although the most progress was surely made by Galileo (1564-1642). If we follow the chronological order of publications, we must, however, give first consideration to a contemporary, Johann Kepler (1571-1630).

Kepler was an assistant to the Danish astronomer Tycho Brahe during the closing years of the latter's life. Although Kepler had little of the master's aptitude for accurate observation, he was able to make a great contribution to astronomy and physics through his mathematical genius. From the data of Brahe, Kepler worked out the orbit of the planet Mars, a task that required four years of computations in which nineteen different paths were tried and rejected before the ellipse was finally accepted. From this painstaking labor, Kepler was able to calculate the orbits of Venus, the earth, Saturn, and to make important generalizations concerning all of the planets of our solar system. Since these laws of Kepler * are the forerunners of Newtonian mechanics it is worth noting them here. First,

---

* See "Stars and Planets" in this *Series,* pages 15 and 16.

Each planet moves around the sun in an ellipse, with the sun at one of the foci. Second, *A planet so moves that an imaginary line drawn from it to the sun (the radius vector) sweeps over equal areas in equal intervals of time.* Third, *The squares of the times that the planets require to make complete orbits about the sun are in proportion to the cubes of their distances from the sun.* The first two laws were enunciated in 1609, the third, nine years later.

While Kepler represents the mathematical physicist, Galileo must be considered primarily as an experimentalist—at least it is in this rôle that he contributed most to physics. Galileo's ingenious study of falling bodies was the opening wedge in the study of mechanics. His "diluting" of gravity by the use of an inclined plane instead of free fall led him to the equation of a uniformly accelerated motion. The very same method is still widely used in teaching the subject today. Further experiments gave Galileo the conception of momentum as the measure of motion of a body. In fact, his *Discourses on the New Science* (published 1638, in Leyden), contains the essence of Newton's First and Second Laws, which we will discuss later.

Since our problem involves time as well as matter, it is interesting to note that the work of Galileo on accelerated motion was performed with aid of a pail of water bearing a small spout—the most accurate method of timekeeping then available. The amounts of water issuing from the spout as the body passed over given distances were weighed. No doubt the difficulty of this method led to the famous pendulum observations. At any rate, after blindness came upon him, Galileo instructed his son and a pupil (Viviani) how to construct a pendulum timekeeper.

However, it is to the Dutch physicist, Christian Huygens (1629-1695), that credit must go for perfecting the mechanism of the pendulum clock as we know it today. To the same genius belongs the honor of first recognizing the difference between weight, the pull of gravity on a body, and mass, the absolute measure of its inertia.* The distinction seems to have first come to him as a result of his careful analysis of uniform circular motion. Here the term "solid quantity" is used. The experi-

---

* See "Energy and Matter" in this *Series.*

ence of Jean Richter, who found his standard clock lost two and a half minutes a day when used in French Guiana though correct at Paris, Huygens correctly surmised to be a result of a lessened earth pull in the region of the equator, albeit the "solid quantity" remained the same.

It may be well at this point to summarize the important work in mechanics so as to gain a better perspective of Newton's contribution. From Galileo came an accurate statement of the relation of a uniformly accelerated motion, and an appreciation of the function of momentum—nearly in the form of Newton's Second Law; from Huygens, an analysis of uniform circular motion and at least a suggestion of inertial mass. Nor should we neglect Kepler's generalizations on planetary motion, though they appear as yet entirely foreign to the picture.

Sir Isaac Newton

From Sir Isaac Newton (1642-1727) came the master-stroke which united these disjointed pieces into one ordered whole— the science of mechanics established on just three laws and one hypothesis! These were:

First Law, *Every body tends to continue in its state of rest or uniform motion in a straight line unless it is acted upon by an outside force.*

Second Law, *Change of momentum is proportional to the impressed force and takes place in the direction of the straight line in which the force acts.*

Third Law, *To every action there is an equal and contrary (opposite) reaction.*

Hypothesis, *Every particle of matter in the universe attracts every other particle with a force that varies directly as the product of the masses and inversely as the square of the distance.*

Such simplification of a vast field of natural phenomena was, until the advent of present-day physicists, deemed the highest goal of scientific progress—a fact that perhaps explains the nearly unapproachable sanctity with which many still regard this work. But one must recall that Newton himself appreciated the incompleteness of the picture; witness these lines from the famous *Principia* (published 1687) :

"Hitherto we have explained the phenomena of the heavens and of our sea by the power of gravity, but not yet assigned the cause of this power. This is certain that it must proceed from a cause that penetrates to the very centers of the sun and planets, without suffering the least diminution of its force; that operates not according to the quantity of the surface of the particles on which it acts (as mechanical causes used to do), but according to the quantity of the solid matter which they contain, and propagates its virtue on all sides to immense distances, decreasing always in the duplicate proportion of the distances.* Gravitation toward the sun is made up out of the gravitations toward the several particles of which the body of the sun is composed; and in receding from the sun decreases in the duplicate proportion of the distances as far as Saturn, as evidently appears from the quiescence of the aphelions † of the planets; nay, and even to the remotest aphelions of the comets, if those aphelions are also quiescent. But hitherto I have not been able to discover the cause of those properties of gravity from phenomena, and I frame no hypothesis; for whatever is not deduced from phenomena is to be called an hypothesis; and hypotheses, whether metaphysical or physical, whether of occult qualities or mechanical, have no place in experimental philosophy."

Miraculous that the assumption of a force between two masses, as described above, should, when taken in conjunction with simple generalizations drawn from experiments on the earth, solve the great riddle of planetary motions!—fitting Kepler's laws to a T. Even more remarkable that the same form of expression should fit electrostatic and magnetic force requirements, is it not? But why does the force exist, and how can it "propagate its virtue on all sides to immense distances" despite the presence of intervening matter? These are questions not answered by the hypothesis.

One characteristic of the Newtonian theory should be stressed for our discussion. The dynamic inertia of a body, *i.e.*,

---

* This is expressed mathematically by the equation $F = G \dfrac{m_1 \, m_2}{d^2}$ where F is the force, G an universal constant, m_1 and m_2 the masses and d the distance between their centers.

† Points of orbits most distant from the sun.

the resistance it offers to motion, is tacitly assumed to be an inherent property in no way related to the surroundings or to the motion of the body. Perhaps the word *tacitly* is not entirely correct, since by the hollow pendulum experiments designed to check the Second Law, Newton showed that the ratio of weight to mass remained constant. However, the velocity range covered was necessarily small and other body effects were always present.

To pass over Newton's work in optics without some comment would be decidedly unfair even though it has little direct bearing on our problem. In this field we find the great mathematical physicist to be of no mean powers as an experimentalist, as evidenced by his classical work on effects produced by a prism. Strangely enough, the phenomenon known by his name, Newton's rings, the formation of colored rings from the reflection of white light in thin films, is today used as one of the arguments against Newton's theory of light. After careful weighing of all evidence Newton felt that a corpuscular action, one depending upon particles, was needed to explain straight line travel of light. He could not conceive a wave motion which would show no more tendency to bend around corners than light. Yet to explain the bending of light in passing through prisms, lenses, and so on, his corpuscular theory required an ether, and so included the same great stumbling-block as the wave theory. So great was Newton's influence, however, that the wave theory, so ably sponsored by Huygens, lapsed into disrepute, thereby retarding the development of optics nearly one hundred years.

THE EIGHTEENTH AND NINETEENTH CENTURIES

The eighteenth century saw no such stimulating development of physics as its predecessor. In mechanics we find little but new mathematical forms given to Newton's laws to render them more adaptable to certain classes of problems.

One of the important products of the early nineteenth century was a clear statement of the principle of the conservation of energy. Count Rumford * expressed a belief that in the boring of a cannon the heat emanated from the mechanical work

---

* Benjamin Thompson, Count Rumford (1753-1814), an American scientist.

LOCATION IN SPACE AND TIME

In order to definitely *fix* any moving object it must be located in *time* as well as in *space*. A flying airplane can be located in space (space in relation to the earth's surface) by means of a map and a barometer reading —at a certain longitude, a certain latitude, and a certain number of feet

above sea level—but this location in space has little meaning without the statement as to *when* it was there. For example, at 1:28 P.M. Pacific standard time, on April 30, 1942. Thus it is clear that any *moving* object must be located in *time* as well as in *space*.

How about an object stationary in respect to the earth's surface—a mountain for example? The answer is that no one can conceive of a mountain lasting no time at all. In order to have any real existence it must last a certain *time*. Any object, in order to be an object, must have extension in four dimensions—length, breadth, thickness, and *duration*.

RELATIVITY OF SPEED OF TIME

On page 17 we saw that everything in the universe could be instantaneously enlarged or reduced without our being aware of it. In a similar way if everything in the universe—the speed of light, the action of bodies in respect to gravitation, our own physical and mental processes—were instantaneously and simultaneously speeded up or slowed down we would never be aware of it; theoretically the universe could be speeded up so that a million years would be as a day without our being conscious that anything unusual had occurred.

Thus we see that *time* is relative.

done. Sir Humphry Davy * vindicated this idea by rubbing two blocks of ice together in a vacuum, the blocks being held by nonconducting rods. The heat required to melt the ice in this case could come from nothing but the mechanical work done. However, the fluid theory of heat was too firmly entrenched to be uprooted by this experiment even though it seems conclusive enough to us.

A German physician, Julius Robert von Mayer (1814-1878), seems to have been first attracted to the concept from his observation that the difference in color between blood in veins and arteries is less pronounced in hot than in cold climes. He attributed this effect to the fact that less energy is needed to keep up body temperature in the former case. Completely fascinated by this idea, Mayer enunciated a generalization of the equality of energy in all possible forms and the principle that energy is indestructible, and that while it may change from one form to another the sum total of all energy in an isolated system remains constant (published 1842) ; *i.e.,* essentially what is known today as the First Law of Thermodynamics. But, inadequately grounded in physics as he was, he could not produce convincing experimental evidence. So it is to the English physicist, James Prescott Joule (1818-1889), that credit goes for establishing beyond question the relationship between mechanical work and heat.

The nineteenth century might well be described as a "period of scientific satisfaction." Theory and experiment were almost too well correlated. The conservation of energy was announced as a general principle and checked in the transformation of work to heat and of mechanical to electrical energy. The English physicist, James Clerk Maxwell (1831-1879), developed an elaborate electromagnetic theory tying together the known wave properties of light and the effects of electromagnetic induction. The German physicist, Heinrich Hertz (1857-1894), soon after succeeded in demonstrating the existence of waves produced from an oscillating electric circuit.

Another example might be given in the field of astronomy.

---

* Sir Humphry Davy (1778-1829), a celebrated English chemist.

Laplace and Lagrange indulged in a protracted controversy concerning the irregularities of the orbits of Uranus and Saturn. The result was a masterful treatment of planetary motions. However, there still remained certain unexplained perturbations of Uranus. A young Englishman, J. C. Adams,* from a purely mathematical calculation based on the known time and amount of these variations together with Newton's laws in the more adaptable forms then available, not only predicted that the cause was an outer planet, but actually described its position in the sky at a definite time. Unfortunately, as the story goes, the Astronomer Royal was out when young Adams called to present his calculations. In the meanwhile Leverrier in France had independently arrived at the same result and communicated with Galle, a German astronomer, who actually found the disk of the new planet, Neptune, in his telescope. What a beautiful verification of Newtonian mechanics!

In passing this remarkably satisfactory confirmation of the exactness of Newton's laws, it is well to note another contribution of Leverrier. In 1859 he noted a motion of the perihelion of Mercury amounting to about forty-three seconds of arc per century. Seemingly a very small thing as compared to locating a new planet, but something that he could not successfully explain on the basis of Newtonian mechanics—just a suggestion of a ripple on the calm of nineteenth century scientific satisfaction!

QUANTUM THEORY †

The closing years of the century witnessed other discoveries destined to mar the completeness of the classical physical reasoning and to stir anew the fires of controversy. Among these was the determination of the ratio of electrical charge to mass for the elementary particle of negative electricity, the work of J. J. Thomson. Max Planck's study of radiation also belongs close to the head of such a list. In 1900, when Planck announced the quantum theory of radiation as a result of this work it was regarded as rank heresy. One professor, present at the meeting

* See "Stars and Planets" in this *Series,* page 29.
† See "Energy and Matter," in this *Series.*

of the Prussian Academy of Sciences when the first public statement was made, rose from his seat saying, "Gentlemen, this is *no* physics," and left the room. An attitude of satisfaction with existing theories which has fortunately disappeared today, was quite generally apparent at this time. The American physicist, Albert Abraham Michelson (1852-1931), in *Light Waves and Their Uses,* published 1910, gave voice to the sentiment by predicting that future generations of physicists would have to content themselves with adding another significant figure to the values of the various physical constants.

The quantum theory as expostulated by Planck satisfied the experimental relation between the temperature of a body and the nature of the radiation emitted by it. This theory postulates that energy occurs in "bundles" of definite size. But so radical an assertion could hardly be expected to gain much credence on this account alone. To say that the energy must attain some fixed value before a body can emit or absorb it, was too foreign to the concept of continuous action, which had been so successful in explaining most electromagnetic phenomena, to be accepted without further confirmation. Indeed since the theory had been built to fit the facts of temperature radiation, its ability to do so can scarcely be regarded as a general confirmation.

At this point (1905) Einstein made two noteworthy contributions. First, he extended the quantum theory to cover the energy relation within the atom or molecule. This gave a satisfactory explanation of the specific heats of bodies at low temperatures—one of the points where measurement and classical theory prediction did not agree. Incidentally it also paved the way for the atomic theory of Niels Bohr. In the second place, as previously mentioned (page 6), Einstein applied the quantum relation to the photo-electric effect, another stumbling-block of classical theory. This work gave confirmatory evidence for the quantum theory that certainly could not be disregarded.

Although not related to his work on the quantum theory the conclusions reached from Einstein's analysis of Brownian movements (see page 6) are interesting in that they modify the

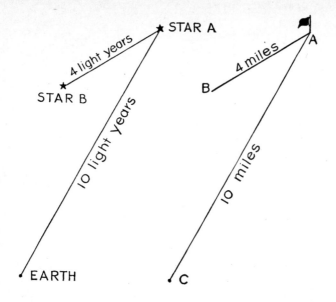

RELATIVITY OF PAST, PRESENT, AND FUTURE

Let us assume that the light from star A traveling at the rate of 186,000 miles per second takes ten years to reach the earth and four years to reach star B. Let us further assume that at a given moment you are observing through a powerful telescope some event happening on star A. Now please note that what you see happening is in the *present* to you— that it is actually a part of *your* present. At no time in your past could you have seen this identical event and at no time in your future will you be able to see it. However that event was ten years in the past to an inhabitant of star A and six years in the past to an observer on star B.

Now let an observer on star B watch an event on star A. It is the *present* to him, it is four years in the *past* to an inhabitant of star A, and it is six years in the *future* to an observer on the earth.

Let us now transfer the experiment to the surface of the earth.

A man at position A waves a flag; you are observing from position C, ten miles away; another observer is located at position B. Neglecting the resistance of the atmosphere, you see the event $\frac{1}{18,600}$ of a second after it happened. The observer at B saw it $\frac{1}{46,500}$ of a second after it happened or $\frac{1}{31,000}$ of a second before you did. The intervals are so minute that for all practical purposes we ignore them and regard light as acting instantaneously. Nevertheless, in reality, the principle of the experiment remains the same and will not change one iota even if we reduce the distances in our earth experiment to ten feet and four feet. The observer at B will see the event at A before the observer at C can see it, although it be but an infinitesimally small fraction of a second between.

interpretation of the Second Law of Thermodynamics,* or, at least, serve to emphasize the fact that it is a statistical relation. Whereas problems dealing with macroscopic bodies † may be treated by such a law, microscopic, or better sub-ultra-microscopic phenomena, cannot, the reason being that in the latter case the number of molecules concerned may be insufficient to permit the application of statistical generalizations. For example, in accordance with the Second Law of Thermodynamics we say that systems tend to a condition of maximum entropy. From a mechanical standpoint this means lowest possible position of the center of mass; yet a colloidal particle in a liquid may move upward because of diffusion due to movement of molecules.

INTERPRETATION OF MODERN ADVANCES

Perhaps the fairest way to describe the progress made during the present century is to say that it has taken the form of pointing out the restricted nature of theories previously considered as general. Thus there has been no contradiction of the old theories, but rather a more complete appreciation of their limited field of usefulness, as typified in the case just mentioned.

Another instance concerns the concept of the conservation of energy, the First Law of Thermodynamics,‡ upon which the first attack was made with the discovery of radioactivity. Here was an example of a group of substances giving off rays capable of producing very considerable amounts of heat energy and, according to the early workers, showing no sign of change or diminution in the rate of energy production. This attack was, however, completely repulsed in 1902 when Rutherford and

---

* "While the various forms of energy are convertible into one another, the conversions do not work equally well both ways. For instance, although mechanical work can be readily and completely converted into heat, the reverse transformation of heat into other forms of energy can be only partly carried out. Let energy once get into the form of heat and it is impossible to get it out again. In most energy transformations heat is a product, and much of it becomes unavailable for further use. Therefore, the proportion of unavailable heat energy in the universe is constantly increasing, and the time will come when no further energy transformations are possible. That is the essence of the Second Law of Thermodynamics."—From *The New World of Physical Discovery* by Floyd Darrow.

† Macroscopic bodies are bodies large enough to be observed by the naked eye.

‡ See "Energy and Matter," in this *Series*.

Soddy demonstrated that radium actually did change as a result of these emanations; in fact, became another chemical element. Thus the energy radiated represents the difference in the internal energies of the two elements, just as the heat generated in the more common chemical reactions is equivalent to the difference in the energies of the compounds before and after the change. But renewed assaults have come from two different angles.   In order to explain the prolonged life of the sun at its high temperature, Arthur Stanley Eddington, the English astronomer, assumed the transformation of matter into energy.   From the opposite side, Robert Andrews Millikan, the American physicist, in his work on cosmic rays, interprets their origin as due to the production of matter from energy, a change assumed to occur in interstellar space.   These considerations lead us directly to Einstein's work on relativity, since both effects are in agreement with his generalizations.   Indeed, since we have already introduced the man in our historical survey, it is about time to pave the way for the entrance of the theory.

THE ETHER

From the publication in 1873 of Clerk Maxwell's famous *Treatise on Electricity and Magnetism* the concept of an ether capable of transmitting light took on new importance.   To be sure, any wave theory of light required a medium by virtue of whose elastic properties the motion could be propagated.   No material substance was known to exist in interstellar spaces, at least not in sufficient concentration to support a wave form, yet light energy obviously permeated these regions.   Thus it became imperative to assume the existence of an all-pervading substance endowed with the desired properties.   Oddly enough even though Newton did not accept the wave theory of light, but rather supported a corpuscular * interpretation, he was unable to discard the "ether"—requiring it to explain the phenomenon of refraction.† However, with so complete and withal so successful an

---

* Corpuscular theory of light, the theory enunciated by Sir Isaac Newton, that light consists in the emission and rapid progression of minute particles or corpuscles.

† Refraction, the deflection from a straight path suffered by a ray of light, of heat, or of sound in passing obliquely from one medium into another in which its velocity is different, as for example from air into water.

hypothesis as that of Maxwell regarding the nature and propagation of all electromagnetic disturbances, every item attracted the attention of physicists, the ether along with the rest.

The French physicist, Armande Hippolyte Louis Fizeau (1819-1896), performed an interesting series of experiments bearing on this topic, of which we shall have more to say later. For the present it will suffice to give the results and note their immediate effect on the trend of electromagnetic reasoning. The work consisted in determining the velocity of light in various transparent fluids moving through a pipe. The conclusion Fizeau reached was that in these cases the ether is carried along with the moving fluid but at a rate somewhat less than that of the fluid. This would suggest that in the case of our atmosphere some ether-drag would exist by virtue of the earth's movement through space.

In 1881, while in Germany, A. A. Michelson tried by experimental methods to determine whether there was any movement of the ether relative to the earth. No such effect was observed. Dr. Michelson was not entirely satisfied that this experiment was conclusive, and in 1887 together with E. W. Morley he repeated the work under better conditions. The method employed depended upon the interference of light waves reflected from two mirrors facing each other. If there is a motion of the ether relative to the earth there should be a shift in the *interference pattern* * produced when the mirrors are turned from a position where their faces are parallel to the direction of the earth's motion to one where their faces are at right angles to this direction. The sensitivity of the apparatus was more than sufficient to show the effect predicted in accordance with the Fizeau experiments, but the result was still negative. A very embarrassing situation!

In 1895, G. F. Fitzgerald and H. A. Lorentz, independently, suggested a way out of the dilemma. The assumption made may be expressed as follows: The measured length of a meter-

---

* Interference patterns originate from the combination of two wave trains. At locations where these light waves strike crest to crest or trough to trough, bright bands are produced; where crest meets trough the effects cancel each other, giving a dark region. A common example of interference is seen when two wire screens are placed one alongside the other so that light must pass through both meshes.

stick becomes *less* if it be given a velocity in a direction along the line of its length. The ratio of the moving value to the stationary value is dependent upon the velocity of the object and of that of light.* As may be noted from the figures given in the accompanying table this effect only becomes appreciable when the velocities approach that of light. This shrinkage of the interferometer arm carrying the two mirrors is just sufficient to make up for the effect of the ether-drift in the Michelson-Morley experiment, an experiment which is explained at length in the next chapter. Presented in this fashion the Fitzgerald-Lorentz contraction theory seems extremely far fetched. Lorentz succeeded, however, in deriving the relation from a theoretical discussion of the electromagnetic properties of matter.

Kaufmann, in 1901, determined experimentally the existence

Table I—CHANGE IN APPARENT LENGTH WITH VELOCITY
OF MOTION

VELOCITY	AMOUNT OF APPARENT SHORTENING
30 miles per hour	1 ten-million-million-millionth of 1 percent
300 " " "	1 million-millionth of 1 percent
93,000 miles per second, *i.e.,*	
½ the speed of light	13.5 percent
182,280 miles per second, *i.e.,*	
98% the speed of light	80 percent
186,000 miles per second, *i.e.,*	
the speed of light	100 percent

of a somewhat analogous effect as regards *mass*. He found the mass of an electron could be changed if given sufficiently high velocities, velocities which cannot be imparted to larger masses. Perhaps "given" is hardly the correct word, since *beta* particles (*i.e.,* electrons) fired from the nucleus of radioactive substances were used. Here the ratio of the apparent mass when moving to the stationary mass also depended upon the velocity of the electron and of that of light, in a manner analogous to the Lorentz contraction. (See Figure 2.)

In both instances the velocity of light acts as a *limiting value*.

---

* The mathematical expression for ratio of the moving to the stationary value is $\sqrt{1 - \dfrac{v^2}{c^2}}$: 1, where v is the velocity of the stick in the direction of its length and c the velocity of light.

At this velocity the measured length of an object would become zero and its mass infinite—both inconceivable conditions. Hence the statement that *speed exceeding that of light is physically impossible.* Indeed the highest velocity with which a material particle has yet been found to move is that of a *beta* particle from radium C, which is equal to $^{98}/_{100}$ that of light.

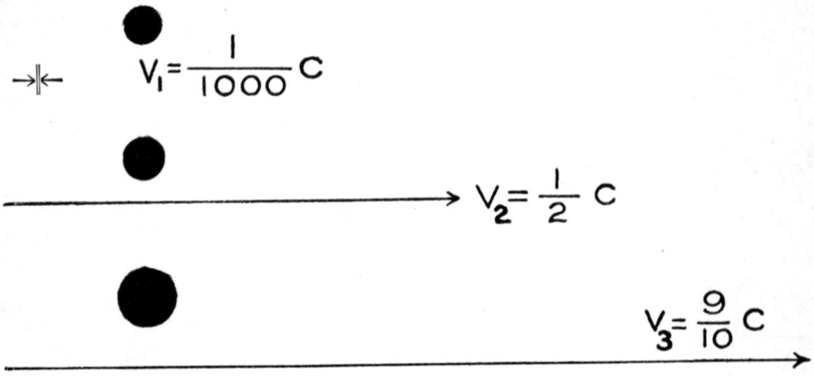

$$V_1 = \frac{1}{1000} \, C$$

$$V_2 = \frac{1}{2} \, C$$

$$V_3 = \frac{9}{10} \, C$$

Figure 2

This figure is designed to show the variation in the mass of an electron with its velocity. In order to make the mass change more obvious, the electron masses have been represented by the areas of circles rather than by the volumes of spheres, as is usually done. The magnitudes of the velocities are represented by the lengths of the lines. The equations indicate the proper pairing of masses and velocities.

If you will recall the state of affairs just prior to the work of Newton you will surely recognize how similar is the stage setting. In the seventeenth century we had the analysis of uniformly *accelerated translation* due to Galileo, the *formulation* for uniform circular motion by Huygens, the empirical statements of Kepler regarding planetary motions, and then Newton's master-stroke that united all into one beautifully comprehensible whole. At the opening of the twentieth century we find the Fizeau experiment, the Fitzgerald-Lorentz contraction theory, the mass variation of Kaufmann and, to jump to the realm of astronomy for an apparently isolated tid-bit, the observations of the French astronomer, Leverrier, in 1859, and of the American astronomer, Simon Newcomb, in 1895, on the perihelion movement of Mercury's orbit—*then*—Einstein!

OUTSTANDING FACTS FROM CHAPTER II

1. The earliest germ of relativity might be found so far back as the fifth century B.C. in the statement of Heraclitus—"You cannot step into the same river twice"—meaning that, though the location be the same, the water would always be different.
2. The Latin poet, Lucretius, pointed out that the universe was infinite and consisted of bodies in space.
3. Aristotle, whose teachings held sway until the seventeenth century, offered no material contribution. The Greek contributions to science came rather from the mind than from the laboratory. It was Roger Bacon (1214-1294) who advocated the experimental method—commonly known as "the cornerstone of modern science"—as the only means to the truth.
4. Kepler (1571-1630) first worked out the orbit of the planet Mars; later he was able to calculate those of Venus, the earth, and Saturn.
5. The discoveries of Galileo (1564-1642) paved the way for the study of mechanics. Although the idea of the pendulum timekeeper is accredited to him, it was Huygens (1629-1695) who perfected the pendulum clock as we know it today. Galileo was also the first to recognize the classical differences between weight (pull of gravity) and mass.
6. Sir Isaac Newton (1642-1727), using the results of previous discoveries, built up and established the science of mechanics on three laws and one hypothesis.
7. Mayer, in 1842, observed that energy is indestructible, and that, while it may change from one form to another, the sum total of all energy in an isolated system remains constant. This is essentially the first law of thermodynamics. Joule (1818-1889) established through experimentation the relationship between mechanical work and heat.
8. The nineteenth century saw science advance in many directions, especially in electricity.
9. The twentieth century brought to light the *quantum theory* of Planck —the suggestion showing that radiant energy occurs in "bundles" or quanta.
10. Einstein, in 1905, extended the *quantum theory* to cover the energy relation within the atom or molecule, and thereby paved the way for the atomic theory of Niels Bohr.
11. Scientific progress in the twentieth century has demonstrated the restrictions of theories previously considered general. There has been no contradiction of the basic truth of the old laws, but rather a more complete appreciation of their limited field of usefulness.
12. Eddington, in accounting for the prolonged life of the sun at its terrific temperature, assumes the transformation of matter into energy; Millikan, in accounting for the origin of cosmic rays, assumes the converse action to be occurring in interstellar space. These theories

of the conservation of energy and of the conservation of mass are merged into Einstein's theory of the conservation of mass-energy.

13. As the Einstein theory deals with velocity, time, and space, former theories and experiments dealing with them are worthy of note:

   a. With the publication, in 1873, of Maxwell's famous *Treatise on Electricity and Magnetism,* the concept of an ether capable of transmitting light waves took on new importance.

   b. Fizeau experimented with the velocity of light through various transparent fluids moving through a pipe, from which he concluded that ether is carried along with the moving fluid, but at a rate less than that of the fluid.

   c. Michelson and Morley conducted a series of experiments, based upon the principle of the interference of light waves, to determine whether there was any movement of the ether relative to the earth, but no such effect was observed.

   d. In 1895 Fitzgerald and Lorentz assumed that the reason for this negative result was because all moving objects shrank in the dimension parallel to their movement.

   e. Kaufmann, by means of experiments, found that the mass of an electron was changed when moving at sufficiently high velocities.

   f. In both the foregoing instances, it is assumed that no speed can exceed that of light, *i.e.,* the velocity of light acts as a limiting value.

14. As the discoveries of Galileo, Huygens, and Kepler paved the way for Newton, so the experiments of the early part of the twentieth century paved the way for the Einstein theory of relativity.

CHAPTER III

THE SPECIAL THEORY OF RELATIVITY

LOCATION AND MOTION

SO FREQUENTLY do we make use of the idea of location that it seems almost childish to inquire into the meaning of the term. But like so many apparently simple things the explanation proves more difficult than one suspects. At first, the answer, "directions that enable another person to reach the place" seems satisfactory. The other "person" here bears the brunt of the attack. What subsidiary knowledge must he have? In many cases a "location" satisfactory for one individual would be decidedly puzzling to another. You say, then, use a map describing the location in reference to a definite point thereon. We are now approaching something like a definite solution. Any point on a map is described by a *latitude,* so many degrees north or south of the earth's equator, and by a *longitude,* so many degrees east or west of the prime meridian through Greenwich, England. Is this our answer?

You immediately think of a position above the earth's surface—the floor of a building, for example. This requires a third piece of information, the number of the floor. Or in more general terms, the height above an arbitrary datum plane, usually taken as sea-level. To obtain this last piece of information might prove difficult in many cases. The methods of triangulation would have to be used to determine the height of a cloud. If we were in an airplane, a barometer reading might be used for an approximate value since the rate of decrease of atmospheric pressure with elevation is known. In each instance we have, in reality, measured an extension of the earth's average radius which is just sufficient to reach the object in question.

For the mathematician the process of locating a point in space is expressed by saying that *any point in space may be located by specifying its three co-ordinates with respect to a given system of axes.* To elucidate: in geographic location you are employing the earth's center as a fixed point taken on the intersection of the equatorial and prime meridian reference planes. The longitude is an arbitrary measure along the circle formed by the intersection of the first of these with the earth's surface; the latitude, a similar measure along the second. The third co-ordinate, at first glance, appears to be missing. It is implied in surface location by the very word surface, *i.e.,* a measure of the earth's radius at that point; and, as described above, an elevated location is given as an extension of this radius. In a more general case all three co-ordinates would be given—the radius value, the latitude angle, and the longitude angle—the system being described by the mathematician as spherical co-ordinates.

For most purposes another system of co-ordinates, known

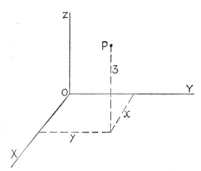

Fig. 3— CARTESIAN CO-ORDINATES

as Cartesians, in honor of the French philosopher and mathematician, René Descartes (1596-1650), is perhaps simpler. In this system a fixed point, or origin, *O,* is taken at the intersection of three mutually perpendicular lines algebraically described as the *X, Y,* and *Z* axes. (See Figure 3.) Throughout the following discussion this method of location will be employed. In visualizing any case it may prove helpful to take a room corner to your left as an origin. The floor will then be the *XY* plane; its intersection with the left-hand wall, the *X* axis; with the wall facing you, the *Y* axis, and the intersection of these two walls the *Z* axis.

MEASUREMENT AND POSITION

No matter which of the many possible systems of co-ordinates be chosen, there remain two arbitrary factors which must be agreed upon before the location values are intelligible: First, the selection of the origin position; second, the measuring unit. In the geographic problem, the center of the earth is the origin, and 1/360 of a great circle (called a degree) the measuring unit. This proves satisfactory enough for the description of places with respect to the earth's surface. You might say for short distances the degree is rather cumbersome, yet it forms the closest approximation to a natural length unit, when taken on the earth's surface, with the possible exception of the wave length of some one of the light disturbances emitted by a specified substance. Indeed the meter (39.37 inches), the basic scientific length unit, was originally designed to be one forty-millionth part of the meridian, although an error in the determination led to the present arbitrary standard.

Suppose the problem to be astronomical—say a description of the orbit of the planet Mercury. Again the earth's center might be used as an origin (as in the Ptolemaic geocentric system). However, due to the motion of this origin an extremely complicated path results. When the sun's center is used as an origin, the result is much simpler. But even the sun is moving. What, then, is the logical point of reference? The answer depends on the issue. In the case of the solar system the best point of reference is its center of mass—approximately that of the sun; for the stars of our Galaxy, its center of mass; and so forth. In no instance is the origin considered necessarily to be absolutely at rest.

Absolute and Relative Motion

The concept of motion has already crept into the discussion. This need not be troublesome, for the path is no more than a succession of positions of the point in question, albeit the term *succession* may not pass without challenge, for this tacitly assumes a new quantity, time. We are again reminded of the expression of the Greek sage, Heraclitus, "You cannot step twice into the same river." We may plot the orbit of the planet Mercury about the sun's center but this does not represent its absolute path in space since the point of reference actually has movement therein. We may be able to determine motion about a given center, and determine the motion of this center about still another center, and so on *ad infinitum,* but what about the final origin? Is it not also in motion?

Having mentioned the combination of motions, let us con-

sider for a moment how this may be done in a few cases. The
normal method of attack is illustrated in Figures 4 and 5. Here

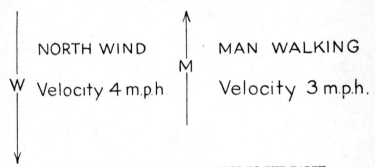

Fig. 4a—VELOCITY WITH REFERENCE TO THE EARTH

The arrow *w* represents the magnitude and direction of the wind; the length signifies a wind
velocity of 4 miles per hour. Similarly the arrow *M* represents the velocity and direction in
which the man is walking. Both arrows, or vectors, have been drawn as they would appear
to an individual at rest on the earth's surface.

each velocity is represented by a line whose length gives the
magnitude of the velocity to some convenient scale and whose
direction is that of the velocity. It will be noted that only where

Fig. 4b—WIND VELOCITY WITH
REFERENCE TO MAN

If we wish to find the effect of the wind
upon the man, we must combine the vectors
of part *a*. The result of the man walking
"into" the wind is to produce an effective
wind velocity for him equal to the wind
velocity with respect to the earth plus his
own velocity with respect to the earth. The
direction of the apparent wind will be the
same as that of the actual wind, in this
case. The construction of the figure indicates this effect, if we say that the magnitude of the apparent wind is represented by
the length of the combined vectors, as shown.

the velocities lie along the same straight line can we say that
their resultant or combined effect is equivalent to the sum of their
speeds. As another illustration of the method we might take

a case which is helpful in considering the Michelson-Morley ether-drift experiment which has already been mentioned as of considerable importance in our discussion of relativity.

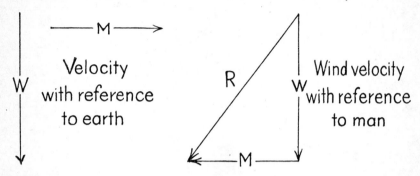

Figure 5

Both vectors represent the velocities with respect to a stationary object on the earth. *Left:* Here we have represented the velocity of the wind as in Fig. 4, but we have changed the direction in which the man is walking. The speeds are the same as in the preceding figure. *Right:* To find the effect of the wind with respect to the man, we combine as before. This requires the reversing of the vector which gives the man's velocity; we are really thinking of the way the air would pass him, even if there were no wind. This assumed wind arising from his motion would have a speed equal to his, but a direction exactly opposite. The effect of the existing wind upon the man is then given by the vector *R;* its direction is indicated by the arrowhead, and its magnitude by the length of the line taken to scale (5 miles per hour).

Consider two motor boats each capable of a speed of 10 miles per hour, in still water, moving in a stream whose velocity is 8 miles per hour. Suppose boat A to travel a total of 24 miles, 12 upstream and 12 back, whereas B goes 12 miles across stream and 12 back, both distances being measured with

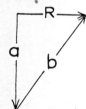

Fig. 6—FINDING THE CROSS-STREAM VELOCITY

a represents the stream velocity of 8 miles per hour; *b* represents the boat velocity of 10 miles per hour; *R* represents the resultant of the stream and boat velocities which was to be at right angles to the stream flow.

reference to the bank. When A is traveling upstream his effective speed with reference to the bank will be only (10 — 8) 2 miles per hour; so that it will take 6 hours to go the 12 miles upstream. But on the return journey the effective speed will be (10 + 8) 18 miles per hour, hence the 12 miles will be covered in only 40 minutes. The total trip for A has been 6 hours and 40 minutes long. In order to find the cross-stream velocity of

B we must resort to vector methods (Figure 6). If the resultant or effective velocity is to be at a right angle to the stream flow, it will be reduced to 6 miles per hour.* Since this speed will hold for both directions, B will require only 4 hours to make the total journey. There is, then, a decided margin (2 hours and 40 minutes) in favor of the cross-stream boat.

MICHELSON-MORLEY EXPERIMENT

In essence this is the principle of the Michelson-Morley experiment; albeit the velocities are very different. Here the "boats" are light waves and have a speed of 186,000 miles per second. In this case the difference in time for the two paths would be very small; for the apparatus used, a .00000000000000075 part of a second. However, the frequency of light disturbances is so great that even this infinitesimal interval would throw the two waves out of step enough to be easily detected by the interferometer. Yet the effect was not found.

We have seen (pages 30-32) how Fitzgerald and Lorentz explained this negative result by assuming that as bodies push their way through the ether they shrink. It should be noted that this shrinkage or compression has been found to be unlike that due to normal applied stress in that it is the same for all bodies regardless of the material from which they are formed. As explained by Lorentz this velocity contraction is an electromagnetic property due to the electrons which are alike in all substances. Although this is an explanation that may be made to fit the facts without departure from the fundamentals of classical theory, it did not satisfy a certain young clerk in the patent office at Bern, Switzerland, one Albert Einstein. His chief criticism was that Lorentz postulated an absolute motion of the earth through the ether. To Einstein there was no precedent to establish such an absolute motion.

---

* This figure, 6 miles, is obtained thus: We know that the sum of the squares of the legs of a right-angled triangle is equal to the square of the hypotenuse; letting x represent the effective velocity of boat B, we have the equation, $x^2 + 8^2 = 10^2$, which by simple algebra becomes $x^2 = 10^2 - 8^2$
$$x^2 = 100 - 64$$
$$x^2 = 36$$
$$x = 6$$

VELOCITY AND MOTION

If a bomb be dropped from a plane, the aviator will see it drop straight to the ground beneath him.   That is, neglecting air resistance, it will always have the same forward velocity as the plane itself, hence will land directly below.   To an observer on the earth, however, the projectile would appear to describe a parabola.   (See Figure 7.)   Which is the true path?   You

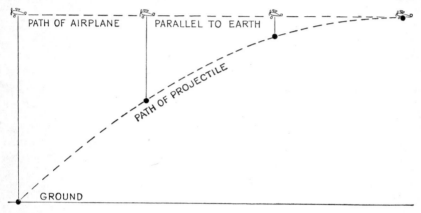

PATH OF AIRPLANE   PARALLEL TO EARTH

PATH OF PROJECTILE

GROUND

Fig. 7—VELOCITY AND MOTION

will probably be inclined to say the parabola.   Suppose, however, our projectile were large enough to be visible from the moon; a lunar observer would scarcely note the forward motion due to the plane nor the drop due to gravitational pull, in comparison to the motion about the earth's axis—an effect entirely unnoticed by the earth watcher because he, too, was being rotated on the earth's surface.   Again, with a pardonable stretch of imagination, suppose an observer on the sun to be able to see our projectile.   To him the motion would seem to be a linear one corresponding to the tangent of the earth's orbit at that instant, this motion being so much more rapid than any of the others as to reduce them to insignificant perturbations.   But the solar observer is not himself at rest!!   What, then, is the true path of the projectile in space?   To Einstein the question is meaningless.   One can only describe the trajectory (path) relative to some specified body on which the system of co-ordinate axis may be erected. *Motion, therefore, is only rela-tive, not absolute.*

THE LAWS THAT GOVERN MOTION

What of the laws which govern the motion just discussed; do they change with a change of reference axes? It would hardly seem reasonable to call them laws if there were no more dependability about them than this. The entire concept of Newtonian mechanics depends on the absolute invariability of these laws. A similar statement could be made for the laws of magneto-optics.* Or perhaps it would be more accurate to say this is the fundamental assumption generally made. Einstein has carried this proposition, in the following form, as one of the basic concepts of his special theory of relativity:

The laws of nature are universal, i.e., their form is invariant and not dependent on the axes used.

The term *laws of nature* may seem obscure. What criterion is there by which to judge? In point of fact, to work the axiom as a test is about the only method. Set up the statement purporting to be a natural law, then switch to any other reference point (moving or not) and determine whether the expression is still in accord with experiment. One, indeed the principal, concept so treated by Einstein in his 1905 paper, was that the velocity of light in a vacuum remained constant (186,000 miles per second). The experimental evidence is the negative result obtained by Michelson and Morley.

VELOCITY AND LIGHT

This premise leads to a difficulty almost immediately. Suppose it were possible for an experimenter to be fired in a rocket capable of a speed of one hundred miles per second. Assume there was a flash simultaneous with the launching of the rocket. In accordance with the method of geometric additions (as illustrated in Figure 4) we would say the velocity of the flash with respect to the projectile would be 185,900 miles per second (186,000 — 100). But to agree with the Einstein assumption,

---

* Magneto-optics, a branch of physics dealing with the influence of the magnetic field upon light.

the velocity of the light should remain 186,000 miles per second with respect to any reference point.   The contradiction can only be removed if we assume that either the measuring rod that we use for measuring distance in the rocket has shrunk one part in 1860; or that the time units there have increased a similar amount; or that both effects have taken place, each to a lesser extent.   The first of these assumptions appears as analogous to the Lorentz contraction; but we shall see that, in reality, the last one really answers this description.

TIME AND SPACE

Unfortunately this particular portion of the relativity treatment can be truly appreciated only as a mathematical truism. To be sure, it is apparent that no *space specification* is complete without a *time value* attached.   You may say an event occurred on the northwest corner of Broadway and 42nd Street, New York, and regard the description as a complete space location. Then you would say the time of the happening was 6:30 P.M. on the 2nd of January, just past, and consider this as a separate specification.   Are not both, however, essential to locate the event completely?   Until the present century, physicists, though conscious of the fact, chose to treat the two as distinct and non-related items.   To a German mathematician, Dr. H. Minkowski, belongs the credit for demonstrating the remarkable relationship between a four-dimensional space-time description, as suggested by the theory of relativity, and the three-dimensional one given in accordance with Euclidean geometry—the four co-ordinates of the first being directly transformable to the three of the common system.

In order to introduce this similarity, and also to answer the problem of retaining the constancy of the velocity of light in a vacuum as a natural law, we must consider the function of *time* in physics in some detail.   Common usage has led us to assume that time is an entity independent of our space representation.   That is, we consider that the time of an event does not vary with the co-ordinate axes chosen.   Suppose we look more carefully into this impression.

For the sake of argument, imagine two men, A and B, a

mile apart, each to fire a gun at a given instant. (We shall return to this problem of simultaneity.) You would then say that an observer, C, midway between the two would hear the reports from each side at the same time. To be sure, this would be some two and one half seconds after the firing, since sound travels with a velocity of some 1100 feet per second. Knowing the observing position to be the midpoint of the line joining A and B, we might employ the fact that the two sounds were heard at the same moment as an evidence that the guns were fired at the same time. The method checks all right for a stationary condition. Now imagine a fourth party, D, to be traveling at a speed of sixty miles per hour (eighty-eight feet per second) toward A, and to be passing C at the instant both guns are fired. Will he hear the reports simultaneously? Obviously not, for he is approaching the disturbance from A but receding from that sent out at B. An algebraic calculation shows that the moving observer will hear the report of A's gun approximately 0.35 seconds before that of B's. Shall we then say the guns were not fired simultaneously with reference to D?

Perhaps your reaction is that the use of sound as a test was unfair. Would you then suggest the sight of the flash as the criterion? An improvement, yes; but light travels with a finite velocity, though a very large one. So that if we give D a sufficiently rapid movement the discrepancy will still appear. What, then, can we say of the term *simultaneous?* Is it not a relative term, in this case true for the stationary observer but not for the moving one? Einstein interprets the effect by saying:

Every reference-body (co-ordinate system) has its own particular time; unless we are told the reference-body to which the statement of time refers, there is no meaning in a statement of the time of an event.

RELATIVITY OF LENGTH

If we now assume that distance measurements are also relative, we have the two necessary conditions to satisfy the restriction that the velocity of light in a vacuum remains constant with respect to a moving system. In his own presentation of the special theory, Einstein does not attempt to vindicate the last

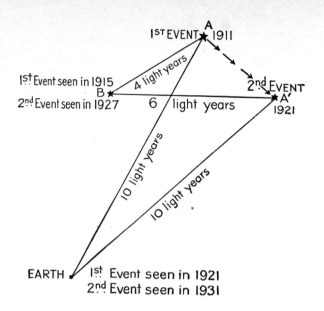

1ST EVENT ★ A 1911

1st Event seen in 1915
B ★
2nd Event seen in 1927   4 light years

6 / light years

2nd EVENT
★ A'
1921

10 light years

10 light years

EARTH ✦   1st Event seen in 1921
2nd Event seen in 1931

RELATIVITY OF TIME AND DISTANCE

Let us now carry on from our star experiment on page 27.

Let us assume that ten years have passed since this experiment and in that time Star A has moved to position A¹. It is still ten light years distant from the earth but is now six light years distant from Star B. You, located on the earth, now observe a second event happen on the Star A¹. You say that the interval between the first and second events is ten years. To make this perfectly clear let us assume that you saw the first event on Star A in 1921. As it took ten years for the light of the event to reach the earth it really happened on Star A ten years before, or in 1911. The second event you saw in 1931, and, as Star A is still the same distance away, it really happened in 1921; that is, the interval between the first event and the second event was ten earth years either for you or for an inhabitant on Star A.

But, how about an observer on Star B? The first event really happened on Star A in 1911. The observer on Star B saw it four years later, or in 1915. The second event really happened in 1921, but it took the light from this event *six* years to reach the observer on Star B, so he saw it in 1927, and states that the interval between the two events is *twelve* years. We could have elaborated the experiment by allowing Star A to have also moved one more light year away from the earth. Then the interval between the events would have been eleven years for the earth observer, twelve years for the Star B observer, and ten years for the Star A inhabitant.

But, you say, if the *distance* between the stars at any given *time* is known, one can calculate the actual interval between events. Yes, but notice that you need a combination of time and distance in order to do this.

45

assumption by any positive reasoning; but rather points out that there is no *a priori* reason to suppose that the separation of two points is an absolute quantity. It seems fair to mention, at least as a suggestive item, the success of the Fitzgerald-Lorentz contraction theory in explaining the result of the Michelson-Morley experiment. A brief analysis of this treatment is given in Appendix I (page 92).

In effect, the Fitzgerald-Lorentz hypothesis assumes the relativity of both distance and time, and the absolute nature of the velocity of light in a vacuum. More precisely, the velocity of light is taken to be identical whether measured with respect to a stationary axis or with respect to another axis moving at any constant velocity. To satisfy this condition we find that a shrinkage of lengths along the direction of motion of the moving system must become apparent to an observer in the stationary system. A converse effect must also take place with the time of the moving region. To an outsider at rest, the ticks of a clock in the moving region would come at longer intervals than if the mechanism were stationary. The nature of both these changes turns out to be such that they are only appreciable for velocities approaching that of light. Another important conclusion is that neither would be apparent to an inhabitant of the moving region.

The behavior of space-intervals, when moving, indicates that a velocity equal to that of light must be the limit attainable. This follows from the mathematical expression (see Appendix I) which would give zero magnitude to the dimension parallel to the direction of the motion for this speed. From the consideration of time in the moving system a similar conclusion might be reached. The Lorentz equations indicate that a second of time in a system moving with the velocity of light would appear infinitely long to a stationary observer, *i.e.*, time would cease to flow—not that it is safe to conclude that a living organism so transported would cease to age, as has often been suggested. To a body in the moving system the clock ticks are still a second apart, and as life would be entirely within the system no difference would exist!

Energy and Mass

Another important relation which Einstein has developed from the special theory of relativity has to do with the conversion of mass into energy, or *vice versa*. A simple mathematical treatment of this topic is given in Appendix II, page 94. We have already noted the variation of mass with velocity, found experimentally by Kaufmann. The nature of this variation is exactly analogous to the behavior of the time-intervals of a moving system—increasing as the velocity of light is approached and becoming infinite when that speed is reached. The effect considered by Einstein is the variation of mass with energy absorbed by it. Obviously such a treatment must reject both the principle of conservation of energy and the law of the conservation of mass. The latter, of course, had already been disproven by Kaufmann's work. What Einstein has done is to fuse the two relations into the same generalization. That is, we should now say that *in an isolated system the sum total of mass plus energy remains constant.*

The results of Einstein's treatment of mass and energy are extremely interesting. He is led to conclude that a body at rest possesses energy by virtue of its mass alone. This is not the usual potential energy that we treat in Newtonian mechanics. The *potential energy* of a mass depends on its position in a field of gravitational force, such as that near the surface of the earth. But the *rest energy* of Einstein is a universal property of the given amount of mass, equivalent to the mass itself times the square of the velocity of light. When energy is absorbed by the mass this rest value is increased by an amount equal to the amount of energy divided by the square of the velocity of light. The square of the velocity of light therefore plays the part of a conversion factor between mass and energy.

The reason that classical mechanics could so successfully ignore this increase in inertial mass with energy absorbed, is that the initial value is so enormous that any energy absorption achieved experimentally is insignificant in comparison. This becomes apparent if we look at some figures given by the late Charles P. Steinmetz. He calculated that, whereas the energy obtainable from one kilogram of coal, by combustion, is equivalent to some ten kilowatt hours, the energy represented by the rest value for this amount of matter (dirt would do as well) is twenty-five thousand million kilowatt hours. He further states: "If the energy equivalent of one pound of dirt could be let loose instantaneously it would be equal in destructive power to over a million tons of dynamite."

Velocity of Light as a Proof of Einstein's Theory

So far we have treated the special theory of relativity as based on a *tested fact* and have drawn a number of interesting conclusions. The tested fact referred to is the negative result of the Michelson-Morley experiment. Although this has been checked by other workers, conflicting results have been obtained. These deserve mention because of the high caliber of the worker, the American physicist, Dr. Dayton Clarence Miller, and the extreme care with which the experiments were performed. Observations made at Mt. Wilson, California, and extending over a period of several years indicated a small but constant ether-drift. No explanation is given for the effect. But even though we grant the correctness of the premises that ether-drift is non-measurable, *i.e.,* that the velocity of light in a vacuum remains a constant for all reference axes no matter what their velocities, this cannot be used as a proof of the accuracy of the special theory of relativity because it has already been used as a basic assumption in the construction of the concept. We must look elsewhere for experimental confirmation.

The experiments of Fizeau on the velocity of light in a moving fluid, performed some fifty years prior to Einstein's theoretical work, deserve consideration. The French physicist found that for this case the velocity of light relative to the tube was not equal to the sum of its velocity with respect to the fluid and that of the fluid with respect to the tube as given by classical mechanics. He gave an empirical formulation which agreed with his experimental results. This expression may be derived on theoretical grounds from relativity considerations. More recent and extremely accurate experiments performed by Zeeman also check the agreement with the relativity theory. One, skep-

INTERSTELLAR NEWS

Printed on the EARTH—Delivered simultaneously to all planets and stars

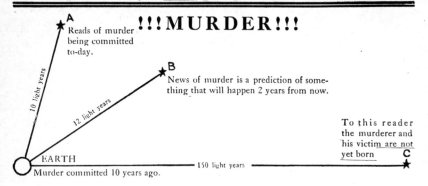

RELATIVITY OF TIME

I pick up a newspaper and it bristles with headlines. Sensational murders, bank robberies, train wrecks, are announced in glaring type. But as I look at the stories I find that they are all old. This murder I remember as having happened ten years ago, this train wreck five years ago, and so on. I call up the newspaper for an explanation; I am told that they have decided to disregard time from now on and state that if I do not consider the items in the paper as news that it is because I am in the wrong place.

Obviously the editor has been reading books on relativity. He is correct. If I were on some distant stellar body, ten light years away, the murder which is now old to me would be just occurring. When I refer to a body ten light years away I mean one which is so far distant that it would require ten years for a flash of light made on this body to reach this earth. As light travels 186,000 miles a second it is evident that it would be a very long distance from us. From the astronomer's viewpoint it is not far. Bodies as far away as 50,000,000 light years have been extensively studied.

If we say that an event has not happened if there is no evidence of it, then to a person more than ten light years from the earth the murder referred to has not yet occurred. To him the newspaper account of the murder would be in the nature of a prediction. If he were much further away the participants in the murder would not yet have been born so far as he was concerned. He would still be seeing events on the earth prior to their birth. Indeed if he were sufficiently far away he might only be seeing the events of Bible times, or even viewing the earth as it was before the coming of men. Thus what is to us the past may elsewhere be the present or even the future. And likewise what may be the past at one place in the universe may be future to us. If we could travel faster than light we could catch up to events that happened years ago and view them once more by means of the light which was reflected from them when they occurred and traveled out into space.

tically inclined, might still remark that there is a similarity between the Fizeau experiments and the Michelson-Morley experiment used in the original hypothesis. Furthermore, Lorentz was able to derive the formula to fit Fizeau's observations from purely electrodynamical relations before the advent of the relativity theory.

As must be already apparent, cases involving velocities approaching that of light would be the ones upon which to test the relativity theory. In the laboratory these restrict themselves to problems involving ions and electrons; chiefly the latter. We have discussed, previously, the work of Kaufmann with electrons fired from radioactive substances. The results obtained here are in good accord with the Einstein prediction. Electronic energy relations may also be studied without having to wait for the electron to leave the atom. Normally this study is made of the outer, or orbital, electrons of the atom. The story is obtained in the form of a picture, called the spectrum, of the atom in question. It would be beyond the scope of this book to discuss the intricate problems of spectrum analysis. Suffice it to say that measurements made on the spectral lines emitted by a given element may be used to predict energy conditions of the electrons within the atom. The key relation is that, due to a combination of Planck's quantum theory with an assumption that an electron emits radiation only after dropping from one fixed orbit to another, closer to the center of the atom, the frequency, or number of vibrations per second, of the radiation emitted is then equal to the energy difference between the two orbits divided by Planck's constant.* For nearly all cases these energy values may be predicted from calculations based on classical mechanics and electrodynamics. Certain lines, however, notably of the hydrogen spectrum, are more accurately given when the relativity correction is applied to the electron velocity. This check is analogous to the Kaufmann experiment but may at least be regarded as a further indication of the inexactness of classical theory.

Marvelous as has been the development of terrestrial physical laboratories during the last hundred years they still cannot

---

* See "Energy and Matter" in this *Series*.

produce the infinite range of conditions to be found in the vast laboratory of the heavens. So one is not surprised to find the majority of the observations offered in verification of Einstein's hypotheses emanating from the field of astrophysics. It is well to note in passing that the intricate complexity of atomic structure yields the other great testing ground already mentioned. The two extremes of human imagination, the super-immense and the sub-microscopic, are thus utilized to prove our theory.

Astronomical Confirmation of the Special Theory

Restricting ourselves to the astronomical confirmations of the special theory of relativity, we find the energy-mass relation to be the crux of the discussion. In the first place the course of stellar evolution can be better explained if we permit the transformation of mass into energy, in accordance with the relation given above, as a consequence of relativity considerations. Our sun, for instance, without this stupendous source of new radiation energy should long since have become cold. During the closing years of the last century this point was the subject of controversy between physicists on one side and geologists and biologists on the other. The latter faction required a much longer period to explain the geologic periods of the earth's history and the processes of evolution than classical physics could permit for the age of the solar system. The discovery of radioactivity * seemed at first to offer a loophole for the physicist. But even were the sun to have been entirely composed of uranium, still the available energy would be too small. The problem is solved very nicely by introducing the concept that *mass and energy are not independent entities but only different manifestations of the same fundamental quantity.*

So much for the change of mass into energy, but the idea of an equilibrium in the universe would suggest that the converse must also take place. Does it? There seems to be justifiable grounds to answer in the affirmative. For many years Dr. R. A. Millikan has conducted a series of experiments on radiations of very short wave length, much shorter than those

---

* See "The Earth" and "Energy and Matter," both in this *Series.*

emanating from radioactive transformations. The frequency of these highly penetrative rays, first noticed by Rutherford and McLennan in 1903, corresponds to the value predicted by the Einstein formula. Some one perhaps asks, "Why should energy be radiated when matter is being formed?" If we assume that hydrogen, the simplest atom, is formed directly from radiation, it is true there would be no reason to expect a radiation. However, in the light of recent chemical and physical investigations it seems more than probable that the heavier atoms are constructed by the aggregation of hydrogen nuclei and electrons. But accurate determinations of the atomic weight of helium indicate that the four hydrogen nuclei present have each lost a portion of its mass. As the chemist would put it, the atomic weight of hydrogen is 1.008 grams, but in the nucleus of other atoms this value is reduced to 1.000 grams. Nor does the loss of electrons account for more than an insignificant fraction of the change. It is to this disappearance of mass (.008 grams divided by 606 thousand million million million, the number of atoms per atomic weight) that the origin of the cosmic rays may be attributed. Millikan feels satisfied that there is no one direction richer in these rays than any other, indicating that they originate in the vast expanse of interstellar space whose extent in all directions is approximately the same. Here, then, is not only another confirmation of the physical truth of Einstein's remarkable mathematical analysis, but also a beautiful balancing action for the old picture of a universe constantly running down.

The Special Theory and Everyday Experience

But you say, "Is there no way in which this great truth affects the everyday contacts of the man in the street? Must we look to either the incomprehensible minuteness of the atom or the equally unimaginable immensity of stellar space for an application of so universal a contention?" The answer is both yes and no. Though every conceivable mechanical effect can be interpreted from the relativity viewpoint, the result in all the familiar everyday relations will for all practical purposes be identical with the conclusion to be drawn from the Newtonian viewpoint. Even the civil and mechanical engineer are not affected. The design for the longest bridge or the highest speed motor would not be changed one iota by the conclusion of relativity corrections. The same might be said for most of the problems of the electrical engineer except where he encounters high speed electrons, as, for example, in special types of vacuum tubes.

Granting that the special theory is principally designed for the physicist and the astronomer, does it completely satisfy their needs? Certainly it comes a step nearer doing so than did classical mechanics; but there still remains a peculiar difficulty. The assumption was that the laws of nature should remain constant in form. For Newtonian mechanics this was only universally possible when a very special type of reference system was used—one at rest. The special theory of relativity improved the situation by permitting the use of reference axes possessed of uniform straight-line motion. But why so restrict the principle? Logically it would appear that the assumption should be more general. Can it be so demonstrated?

OUTSTANDING FACTS FROM CHAPTER III

1. *Location* is estimated by a system of co-ordinates or references in a number of ways; the two most common are:
   a. By spherical co-ordinates, using the earth's center as a fixed point, it is calculated from three references:
      (1) The latitudinal angle,
      (2) The longitudinal angle,
      (3) The radius (*i.e.,* the measure of the earth's radius and height above sea-level at the point in question).
   b. By the Cartesian system of co-ordinates—a point being located by its distance from three mutually perpendicular lines.
2. Astronomical locations are difficult to calculate due to the fact that the earth's surface and the sun's center are used as fixed points, neither of which bodies is at rest. This brings to light the element of time as a dimensional factor, which must be included in calculations of this nature.
3. The explanation of the negative result of the Michelson-Morley experiment by Lorentz—that all bodies are compressed when forced through ether—did not satisfy Einstein, who was then a clerk in the Swiss Patent Office. He criticized Lorentz's premise of the earth

having an absolute motion through ether. Einstein claimed that there was no precedent to establish *absolute* motion and claimed that all motion was *relative*.

4. One of the basic concepts of the Einstein theory of relativity is that "the laws of nature are universal—their form is invariant and not dependent on the axes used." A law of nature, for example, is that the velocity of light in a vacuum remains constant, *i.e.,* 186,000 miles per second.

5. In physics the element of time is highly important, for no space specification is complete without a time value attached. It was only with the beginning of the twentieth century that Minkowski demonstrated the remarkable relationship between four-dimensional space-time and the three-dimensional space of classical geometry and the fact that one system could be mathematically transformed into the other.

6. The special theory of relativity rejects the laws of energy and mass conservation, but establishes the theory that, although the mass or energy taken separately may vary, the sum total of mass plus energy remains constant. Einstein contends that the rest energy of a body is a universal property of matter, equivalent to the mass itself times the square of the velocity of light. This is not the usual potential energy, which depends upon its position in a field of gravitational force. Here it may be seen that the velocity of light plays an important part in the conversion of mass into energy and energy into mass.

7. The great testing ground of the Einstein theory is confined to super-immense and sub-microscopic dimensions and with velocities approaching that of light. For ordinary speeds the Einstein theory makes no appreciable change in Newtonian formulas.

8. In the astronomical field, the Einstein theory of the transformation of mass into energy is able to account for the great length of time needed in the explanation of stellar evolution. Our sun, for instance, without this assumed source of new radiation energy, should long since have become cold.

9. Millikan, in his experiments with *cosmic rays* (the shortest and most powerful known), is satisfied that these rays are no richer from any one direction than from another. Hence he concludes that such rays originate in the vast expanse of interstellar space, the extent of which is approximately the same in all directions. The idea not only supports the Einstein theory, but balances the old conception of a universe which is running down.

CHAPTER IV

THE GENERAL THEORY OF RELATIVITY

IN THE preceding chapter we emphasized the fundamental idea which led to the statement of the special theory of relativity, namely, *that the formulation of a natural law should be unaltered by a change of reference axes.* (See page 42.) For classical mechanics this was true only when the frames of reference were at rest with respect to each other. The effect of the refinements introduced by the original theory of Einstein was to extend the interchangeability to include axes having a uniform, straight-line motion. There still remains a very great restriction upon the utility of the fundamental concept. We can conceive of a great many bodies, upon which we might wish to place the origin of our co-ordinate system, only to find that their non-uniform motion necessitated a reformulation of the physical problem to be treated.

Let us look for a moment at the interpretation of this restriction. Imagine yourself to have been dozing in your seat near the window of a train. Suppose when you awake and look out, there is another train alongside. Can you judge your own movement by observing your neighbor at the window of the other train? If you remain opposite each other, does it mean that you are at rest, or that you and your neighbor are both moving in the same direction at the same speed? Only the sound of the locomotives, or of the car wheels will decide. If your neighbor gradually drifts past you, does that mean you are stationary and that he is moving slowly by; or that both trains are moving in the same direction, his faster than yours; or is he perhaps stationary while you are backing? Mere observation of the relative motion will never help you to decide. So long as your train is either at rest or traveling with a constant velocity you will not be aided in making your decision by consideration of anything within your own car. We say, therefore, that the states of rest and uniform motion are *per se* indistinguishable. There is, then, no logical reason to ascribe to a state of rest the unique property given by the Newtonian mechanics. The special theory of relativity follows naturally enough.

But suppose your train were being accelerated forward— what then? Your umbrella hanging on the hook overhead would swing to the rear. You would feel yourself pushed against the back of the seat. A drop of moisture on the inside of the window-pane would not run straight down, but would be deflected toward the rear, describing a parabolic path. In short, you can readily sense the existence of the acceleration without any observations outside your own reference system, the train. Here is a distinct variation from the case considered above. The behavior of bodies is obviously different in the accelerated system than in the stationary, or uniformly moving one. It would, therefore, seem improbable that the same descriptions should hold in the two cases. In other words, our original assumption of the invariance of natural laws, as shown in Chapter III, apparently meets a pitfall here.

FORCE AND GRAVITATION

To extricate ourselves from this difficulty, let us consider in detail the cause of the difference. Newton's Second Law (see page 20) tells the story: Where there is an acceleration, there is a force acting, and the acceleration is proportional to this force, the factor of proportionality being the *inertial* mass of the body, *i.e.,* the measure of its resistance to change of motion.

This explanation is clear enough so long as we imagine a force directly applied to a body—the pull of the locomotive upon the train, for example. But there are a great many cases in which no such tangible force is evident. Consider an apple falling from a tree, or the moon describing its orbit. Both are due to the gravitational pull of the earth, you say. But you must surely grant there is a big step from the simple expression of the Second Law to this somewhat mystical invocation of the great genie, gravity. Are you certain that this is the only possible explanation? Must we say that every bit of matter in the universe attracts every other with an invariant force proportional to the products of the respective solid quantities and inversely proportional to the extent of their separation? An answer to this question entails a further digression into the nature of such an action. As an opening wedge we ask ourselves, "Is there any analogous action within the realm of our experience?"

Oddly enough two similar effects occur in nature, both of which at first seem much more obscure in their nature than gravitation, but of whose origin and action we are nevertheless somewhat better informed. These are the electric and magnetic forces associated with matter. Perhaps it is the fact that either or both of these forces may be removed from a given laboratory problem, making their analysis easier than that of the more ubiquitous * property treated by Newton. At any rate we feel more confidence in our explanations of their behavior even if we are equally in the dark as regards their true origin.

The interpretation, given to either the electric or the magnetic phenomena by Faraday in terms of force in the media surrounding the electrically charged or the magnetic body has been so successful as to become universally accepted. In accordance with this idea we say that surrounding such bodies there exists a *field of force*. By virtue of this field other charged or magnetic bodies are influenced. To be sure, this is by no means an explanation of the action. However, this idea of a strain existing always in the surrounding ether is more satisfactory than imagining a force to suddenly come into being when a body is brought to the location in question—the older action-at-distance-theory.

But what of the response to this force, does it vary with the origin of the force? For a given magnitude, is the action of a body one thing for an electric force and another for a magnetic force? As you doubtless know, the answer is that Newton's Second Law holds for both cases. The acceleration acquired will equal the force divided by the inertial mass of the body. This inertial mass is not a function of the nature of the force acting, but a constant for the body (if we neglect the mass variation with velocity discussed under the special theory of relativity).

* Ubiquitous, existing everywhere at the same time.

The Gravitational Field

Now we come to the gravitational field. Again we can calculate its intensity at any point in space and consider the effect on any body placed there just as for the electric or magnetic case. Again the measure of the effect produced will be the inertial mass of the body in question. Nothing unusual in this. But let us look at the method used to arrive at the field intensity.

The *field intensity is defined as the force on a unit of the susceptible quantity placed at the point in question.* Hence the electric field intensity is a measure of the force on a unit electrostatic charge; the magnetic field intensity, the force on a unit magnetic pole; the gravitational field intensity, the force on a unit of gravitational quantity. Approached from this angle, there is no *a priori* reason to suppose this gravitational unit to bear any relation to the quantity called one gram of inertial mass, any more than does one electrostatic unit of charge or one electromagnetic unit of pole strength. However, the most careful experiments yet performed indicate that the two are identical, or certainly not at variance by more than one part in 200,000. There is something here which will bear careful consideration. Such a coincidence can hardly be fortuitous.

Let us borrow a lead from Einstein himself in order to investigate the possible origin of this identity of the thing called gravitational mass and the measure of resistance to change of motion, the inertial mass of a body. Suppose the room in which you now sit could be removed intact to an imaginary region devoid of all that we classify as gravitational action. Arrived there, let it be attached to a pulley system so that it can be given an "upward" acceleration, *i.e.*, along the direction of a corner from floor to ceiling. Let this acceleration be thirty-two feet per second per second—that of gravity in its former habitat. Had this transition occurred while you slept, and were the room completely isolated from its surroundings, would any change be apparent to you?

Adhering to the condition of complete isolation, the mechanical relations holding within the room yield the only possible clues. Suppose you release this book from your outstretched hand, will it "fall" to the floor? An outside spectator, appreciating what was really happening to your room, would say that when you released the book the force necessary to give it the acceleration common to all the other objects of the room was removed. It would then continue onward with a uniform velocity; but since the rest of the surroundings are still being accelerated, it would drop back with respect to them. To you this dropping back would manifest itself as an acceleration toward the floor equal to thirty-two feet per second per second, exactly as would have happened when the room was on the earth's surface.

Again, suppose you have a platform scale at hand; if you step upon it, will the reading be the one to which you are accustomed? In order to maintain your position with reference to the rest of the enclosure, a force equal to the product of your inertial mass by the common acceleration, thirty-two feet per second per second, must be supplied by the object on which you rest. But this force is exactly equivalent to the "pull" of gravity upon you when back on *terra firma;* so that the reading of the scale will not be altered.

You might try any number of these mechanical experiments, but they would all suggest to you that conditions were identical with those on the earth; although, in every case, an outsider would appreciate that they were due to the acceleration of the room. The similarity of the two viewpoints gives us an inkling of the physical meaning of the statement that the gravitational and inertial masses of a body are the same. However, Einstein warns us against assuming that all gravitational fields are necessarily only apparent, as in the case just described. At least we must bear in mind that, in most instances, no set of axes can be so located that the gravitational field will disappear.

Behavior of Light in a Gravitational Field

Before we leave this accelerated-room analogy, let us consider the behavior of a light beam therein. Let the light rays be traveling in a direction parallel to the floor of the room and assume that they enter through a small aperture at A. (See Figure 8.) Experience tells us that, if the room were stationary, these rays would strike the opposite wall at B, having followed a straight-line course across the room. When the room is being accelerated, however, the path would no longer be a straight line with respect to an observer within the room. The spectator and all objects around him, except this light beam, are

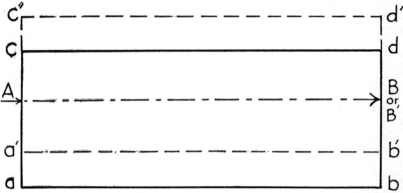

Fig. 8a—THE ACTUAL PATH OF A LIGHT BEAM IN AN ACCELERATED ROOM
The displacement of the room is assumed to be from the position *a b c d* to *a'b'c'd'* in the time required for the light beam to cross the room.

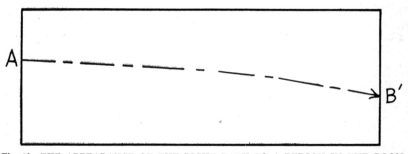

Fig. 8b—THE APPEARANCE OF THE LIGHT PATH TO A PERSON IN THE ROOM

possessed of an acceleration. Therefore, just as with the book released from the hand, the light beam would drop back with respect to the room. Its path would therefore be parabolic, striking the wall at B' instead of at B.

In other words, the path of an electromagnetic radiation is not straight when it passes through a gravitational field, for we have agreed that the accelerated room would be so interpreted by an inmate. In practice, this conclusion is not easily checked because of the extremely high velocity of light in comparison to the acceleration associated with any known gravitational field. For rays passing the sun at grazing distance the deflection from a straight path comes out to be 1.7 seconds of arc. Small though this deviation is, it is nevertheless measurable. In a later paragraph we shall treat of the experimental confirmation of this prediction.

Some one is already murmuring, "But you have emphatically stated that the velocity of light remains constant with respect to a moving axis. This has been introduced as the leading concept in the special theory of relativity. Then on broadening the theory to cover accelerated as well as uniform motions, you immediately controvert the idea; for a curved light path necessarily means a variable light velocity."

The criticism is no doubt a fair one, albeit Einstein gives a satisfactory explanation. The fundamental concept of the relativity theory in its broadest sense is the *invariability of the laws of nature*. Now, so long as one considered only regions free from gravitational fields, the constancy of the velocity of light might be treated as one of these natural laws. This treatment is not, however, valid for regions in which gravitational fields do exist. There is nothing startlingly illogical about such a change. We have long known that the velocity of light in material media is less than that in a vacuum, and further, that it varies from substance to substance, as witnessed by the phenomenon of refraction.

Properties of Space

Recognizing that a region whose characteristics are such as to produce so fundamental a change as a curvature of light might also lead to other remarkable deviations from the usual, let us investigate more carefully. Suppose we imagine a vast number of our accelerated rooms, each placed at a slight angle to its neighbor so as to form a large circle, comparable to the earth's equator, if you please. Provided we keep the accelerations upward and perpendicular to the respective floors, the whole system may be regarded as an approximate analogy to the radial gravitational field of the earth. Let us further imagine a circle to pass through the entire system. If some super being measured the circumference of this immense loop, and also its diameter, would he obtain the usual relation, circumference equals π times the diameter where π is equal approximately to 3.1416? The conception of measuring units gained while considering the special theory of relativity helps us here. When measuring along the circumference the work is done perpendicular to the direction of motion, so that the normal value would be obtained; but in determining the diameter of this great circle, assuming it to be fixed and stationary, the measurement is along the line of motion of the room, so that the measuring rod would be subjected to the velocity contraction. That is to say, whereas the regular number of units would be found in the circumference, the number in the diameter would be more than the rest value. Hence it follows that the circumference is less than π times the diameter.

At first this property of gravitational field space seems truly remarkable. Further consideration shows that the idea is not really new to us at all. Suppose all the points 1000 miles distant from New York to be joined by a circle. The circumference of this circle will be approximately 1980 π miles (i.e., 1 percent less than π times 2000). The reason is apparent from Figure 9; the diameter has been measured over the curved surface of the earth and is therefore greater than the straight line joining its extremities, which in plane geometry would have been called the diameter of the circle. The

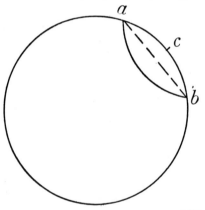

Fig. 9—RELATION BETWEEN A DIAMETER MEASURED ON A SPHERICAL SURFACE AND THE SHORTEST DISTANCE BETWEEN ITS END POINTS
With c as a center a distance ac is laid off in all directions on the spherical surface. The circle so formed will have a circumference less than πacb, since in Euclidean geometry its diameter would be taken as the straight line ab.

difference would become more pronounced if a larger radius were used. In fact, had a radius equal to half the earth's circumference been taken, there would be only one point on the circle, i.e., its circumference would be zero. You recognize the result to be typical of spherical trigonometry. Indeed we shall find it convenient to think of the properties of the three-dimensional space of the gravitational field in terms of its more familiar two-dimensional analogue.

The principles of spherical trigonometry have already shown the possibility of relations not in agreement with those of Euclidean geometry. A few other discrepancies are worthy of note. In plane geometry the sum of the angles of a triangle equals 180 degrees; but when a three-sided closed figure is drawn on the surface of a sphere, the sum of the interior angles measured on the curved surface is always greater than 180 degrees and may approach as much as six right angles (Figure 10). Again, a straight line drawn on such a surface is not infinite in length, although it has no ends. Imagine a line

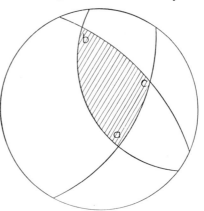

Fig. 10—A SPHERICAL TRIANGLE
In spherical geometry the three angles of a triangle always equal more than 180°.

to pass through New York in an east-west direction. If you should start to measure its length from New York and traveling westward, you would find yourself back at the starting point after covering some 18,900 miles, the circumference of the circle of latitude at New York.

Still another important difference between the two cases arises in the consideration of parallel lines. Suppose we have established a north and south line, a meridian, through a given location. To obtain a parallel to this through a position external to it, we would again fix upon the meridian at the new local. But a definition of parallelism, in accordance with Euclid, requires no intersection. This is not true for our two meridians, since they will cross at the north and south poles.

CURVED SPACE

This is all very fine for a two-dimensional problem, but what does it all mean as applied to space? A curved surface is common enough in experience; but what is curved space? The term defies visualization because we are three-dimensional beings. How do we appreciate the curvature of a surface? Certainly only by use of a third dimension against which to judge it. Suppose us to be a race of two-dimensional beings, restricted to a tiny sector of an isolated spherical globe; what possible means would we have of appreciating its shape? In such a case we might have developed a system of geometry similar to that of Euclid which would appear to hold on the surface of our earth. That is to say, such beings would imagine their habitat to be a plane. In point of fact, primitive human races were in much this position despite the availability of a third dimension to them. Now, should our restricted peoples eventually spread over the entire surface of their globe and become able to make measurements over its entirety, they might discover the relations which we used in spherical trigonometry. Even so, their peculiar form would render the appreciation of the cause of these relations impossible, except as mathematical truths. They could not pass a straight line through the interior of their globe to show that it was shorter than one drawn on the surface between the same terminal points. Thus it is with a three-dimensional being approached with the conception of curved space. There is no fourth dimension through which he may pass a straight line to illustrate that a line drawn in his three-dimensional universe is not the shortest distance between two points therein.

It will be recalled that in the preceding chapter the interrelation of space and time discovered by the mathematician Minkowski satisfied the requirements of the special theory of relativity. Further considerations have shown that the problem then treated was one in which gravitational fields were absent. That is to say, the "universe" of the special theory of relativity would be classified as a four-dimensional Euclidean continuum. As might be expected, the more complete analysis of the general theory still requires a four-dimensional universe, albeit not an Euclidean one. Nor can this latter continuum be described by the cubical space blocks of the Cartesian system of co-ordinates. As shown when the problem was first discussed, a space to be

THE APPARENT SLOWING UP OF TIME

Imagine a huge clock whose single hand makes a revolution in twelve seconds. Suppose this clock is traveling in a straight line with the speed of light from a similar stationary clock where an observer is located. Suppose the moving clock to possess a mechanism which automatically

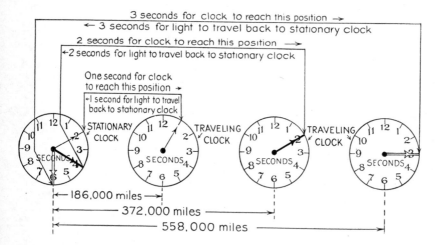

illuminates the hand each second, the clocks to be synchronized, and the hand of each to be at twelve as the journey commences. At the end of the first second the moving clock is 186,000 miles away and its hand lights up. The rays of light from this illumination take one second to reach the stationary observer. When they reach him the hand of his clock is at two. At the end of two seconds the moving clock is 372,000 miles away. The rays of the illuminated hand now take two seconds to reach the observer and thus arrive as the hand of his clock is at four. The moving clock would appear to the stationary observer to be running just half as fast as his own.

According to *orthodox* physics this is what the observer would expect, but according to Einstein's formula the hand of the moving clock would appear to remain stationary at twelve.

described by Cartesian co-ordinates must satisfy the properties of parallelism given in Euclid. Where this is not the case, a more general treatment is required. A method due to the mathematical physicist Gauss is the one used. It would be beyond the scope of this book to consider Gaussian co-ordinates in detail. Suffice it to say the method makes it possible to assign four arbitrary values to each position in the four-dimensional gravitational field-space in such a manner that neighboring points will differ by infinitesimally small amounts. When the universe is so treated the general principle of relativity holds—in Einstein's words, "All Gaussian co-ordinate systems are essentially equivalent for the formulation of the general laws of nature."

A FINITE UNIVERSE?

As already stated, a physical conception of the state of affairs just described is necessarily denied to a three-dimensional being. Nor would it be wise to attempt to treat here the manner in which the origin of its properties may be found mathematically. There are, however, several interesting conclusions to be drawn regarding the physical nature of such a universe. To these and to the experimental evidence in their support, the remainder of the chapter will be devoted.

Let us consider first the extent of our universe. We are reminded of the expression attributed to Epicurus, some three centuries before Christ, "Again, the universe is infinite, for the finite has an extremity which can only be observed against something else, which is impossible in the case of the universe." This reasoning seems fair enough. Yet we cannot suppose that the number of stars is also infinite, if we are to adhere to the inverse square law of mass attraction given by Newton. The reason may not be immediately obvious, but it follows from consideration of the force relations of a group of particles. In fact, Newtonian mechanics would suggest the existence of a center for the universe where the average density of matter is greatest. Traveling outward from this region the number of stars encountered in a fixed distance would become fewer and fewer; until, at a great distance, there would be only empty space. The observed blackness of the sky also leads to the conclusion that the number of stars must be finite.

Astronomical evidence does not seem to support this type of star arrangement. The appearance seems to be that the average promiscuity of stellar matter is everywhere the same. This does not mean that all stars have the same density; in fact they vary between such wide limits as 1/1,000,000 of the density of water for Betelgeuse, and 60,000 times the density of water for the companion of Sirius. Nor does the statement mean that there are no such things as star clusters, for one of the greatest of the recent achievements in astronomy has been to demonstrate the existence of island galaxies within our cosmos. The implication merely is that there is no regular attenuation of these stellar bodies along some one direction as suggested by Newtonian mechanics.

The curvature of gravitational space suggested by the general theory of relativity, yields a possible solution to this contradiction between mass action and the distribution of stars. We must now concede that the reasoning of Epicurus loses force; the universe might be finite and yet have no limits. Certainly this is apparent enough in the two-dimensional cases we have so often used for comparison. The surface of our earth is an example of a two-dimensional continuum of definite extent yet having no end points. It does become difficult to conceive of a similar condition in three dimensions; but the trouble is only with our imaginative powers.

SIZE OF THE UNIVERSE

Einstein has given a formula by means of which the radius of the spherical universe may be calculated. The observational factor in this relation is the average density of the universe. Steinmetz, assuming the average distance between stars to be 40 light years * and their density to average that of water, calculated the radius of the universe to be 100,000,000 light years. This makes the volume of the universe 4×10^{63} cubic

---

* Light year, the distance light travels in one year—about six million million miles.

miles;*—a figure that, at first, does not seem remarkably large for so gigantic a dimension. But again our imagination is powerless to grasp the problem. Listen to the way in which Steinmetz attempted to give some reality to the size of this mensuration.

"The expression 4×10^{63} does not look so formidable, but let us try to get a conception of it—for instance as cents. How long would it take to count 4×10^{63} cents in money? To expedite the process we may count not in cents, nor in dollars, nor in hundred-dollar bills, but in checks, as a check can be made out for a larger amount of money than any bill. We can count out about two checks per second. Let us then make these checks as large as imaginable—make each out for the total wealth of the earth—that is, the total value of all cities and villages, all fields, forests, mines, and factories, all ships and railroads, in short everything existing on earth, hundreds of thousands of millions of dollars.

"Suppose we count out two checks per second, each for the total wealth of the earth, and count out such checks continuously, twenty-four hours per day, week days, Sundays, and holidays, and get all the thousand millions of human beings on earth to help us count out such checks, and do that from their birth to their death without ever stopping, and assume that hundreds of thousands of years ago, when man developed from his ape-like ancestors, he had been put to work to count such checks, and throughout all its existence on the earth the human race had spent every second to count checks, each for the total wealth of the earth, then, the total amount of money counted out, compared with 4×10^{63} cents, would not be so large as an acorn is compared with the total earth."

On this basis we may readily see that the universe is infinite so far as human perception goes. Yet mathematically there is an important difference, and by working backward we can give a physical consequence which is certainly not without meaning. An infinite universe would require the complete absence of matter. Although the estimated density, if all matter was evenly

---

* The figure 4 followed by 63 ciphers. For an explanation of this exponential form for very large or very small numbers see "Energy and Matter" in this Series.

CURVED SPACE

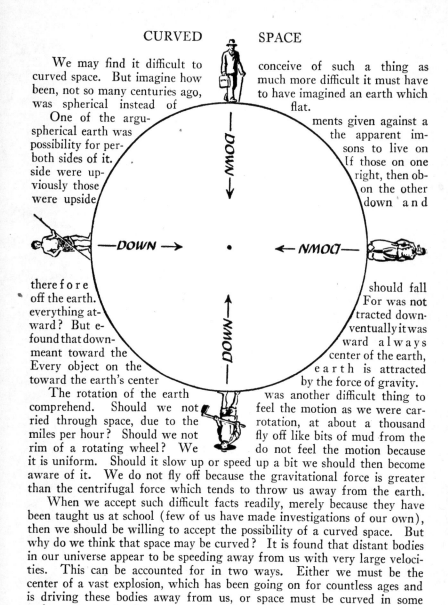

We may find it difficult to conceive of such a thing as curved space. But imagine how much more difficult it must have been, not so many centuries ago, to have imagined an earth which was spherical instead of flat.

One of the arguments given against a spherical earth was the apparent impossibility for persons to live on both sides of it. If those on one side were upright, then obviously those on the other were upside down and therefore should fall off the earth. For was not everything attracted downward? But eventually it was found that downward always meant toward the center of the earth, and every object on the earth is attracted toward the earth's center by the force of gravity.

The rotation of the earth was another difficult thing to comprehend. Should we not feel the motion as we were carried through space, due to the rotation, at about a thousand miles per hour? Should we not fly off like bits of mud from the rim of a rotating wheel? We do not feel the motion because it is uniform. Should it slow up or speed up a bit we should then become aware of it. We do not fly off because the gravitational force is greater than the centrifugal force which tends to throw us away from the earth.

When we accept such difficult facts readily, merely because they have been taught us at school (few of us have made investigations of our own), then we should be willing to accept the possibility of a curved space. But why do we think that space may be curved? It is found that distant bodies in our universe appear to be speeding away from us with very large velocities. This can be accounted for in two ways. Either we must be the center of a vast explosion, which has been going on for countless ages and is driving these bodies away from us, or space must be curved in some such way as to deceive us regarding the motion of these bodies. Of the two possibilities the latter seems the easier to believe even though we are able to form no concrete picture as to just what curved space might look like.

distributed throughout the universe, is only 3×10^{-25} times that of water, still the universe is certainly not entirely devoid of material substance.

THE WARPING OF SPACE

Although no direct confirmation can be expected for this conception of the extent of the universe, it appears in harmony with recent astronomical work. Edwin P. Hubble of the Mt. Wilson Observatory, states that the largest present-day telescope reaches into space a distance of 300 million light years. In this region some thirty million island galaxies have been found, each similar to the Milky Way system of which our own sun is a part. The apparent speeds of the more distant of these clusters, in general, run high and are directed away from us. For one in the bowl of the Great Dipper a value exceeding 7000 miles per second has been obtained.

These high recessive speeds might be interpreted as apparant only, being produced by the curvature of space. If this be the case, the warping of space would have to be viewed against a fourth dimension. Some conception of the effect may be gained from the consideration of a line of sight. In the gravitational field, called by mathematicians "elliptic space," a straight line has a finite length. In other words, a line of sight would return to the back of your head were there no absorbing media in its path. The length of the circuit would be the universe circumference, some 400,000,000 light years, in accordance with the data previously used.

GRAVITATIONAL SPACE AND TIME

Another property of the gravitational field, as predicted by Einstein, has reference to time units therein. In discussing the special theory of relativity we noted that a clock on a moving axis would appear to run slow as viewed by a stationary observer. A clock in a gravitational field should exhibit the same property, following the accelerated motion analogy previously given. Now, although it is not possible for us to place clocks on the fixed stars to check this action, natural time-keepers happen to be already available there. The various atoms emit spectra which have been carefully studied in terrestrial labora-tories. Since the velocity of these light disturbances is constant their measured wave-length differences may be directly inter-preted as differences in the frequencies of the emitters. In short we may think of the electron which yields a given spectral line as a time-measuring device. If its period is slowed down, the wave length in question becomes longer, *i.e.*, is displaced toward the red end of the spectrum. (Wave length equals velocity divided by frequency.*) The effect should be most noticeable in an extremely high gravitational field such as that of the companion of Sirius. But it must be separated from a similar displacement due to the motions of the star in the line of sight. (The Doppler effect.*)

Perihelion Movement of the Planet Mercury

We have purposely treated first those predictions of the general theory of relativity in whose support the evidence is most questionable. We have followed the method of the lawyer who saves his strongest arguments to the last that the retiring jurymen may have the essential facts fresh in their minds. So it is that we now approach the two considerations which have been most effective in establishing the general theory of rela-tivity: 1, The displacement of the perihelion of Mercury's orbit, and, 2, The curvature of light passing near the sun's disk.

Einstein has shown that when the general theory is applied to a system in which all gravitational fields are assumed to be very weak and in which all masses move with velocities negligibly small in comparison to that of light, Newtonian mechanics is ob-tained as an approximate solution. Furthermore, this result fol-lows without having to assume the inverse square law of mass attraction as Newton did. We have called this an approximate solution. As it turns out, however, the inaccuracies so intro-duced are for the most part so small as to defy experimental detection.

One deviation from Newtonian calculation had been noted as early as 1859 by the French astronomer Leverrier. The classical theory for the orbits of the planets yields ellipses whose

---

* See "Energy and Matter" in this *Series*.

axes should remain fixed with respect to the system as a whole when a correction is made for the action of other planets. But Leverrier noted a movement of the axis of Mercury's orbit of about forty-three seconds of arc per century. In 1895 Newcomb checked this observation. A small matter, about twenty miles out of more than one hundred million, but one which Newtonian mechanics did not satisfactorily explain. Some effort was made to attribute the effect to another planet which had hitherto escaped detection because of its close proximity to the sun. The

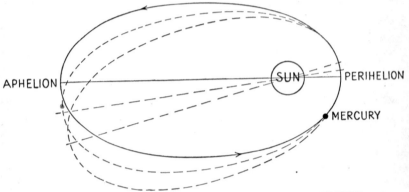

Fig. 11—PERIHELION MOVEMENT OF THE PLANET MERCURY

suggestion has been thoroughly discredited because no other evidence was forthcoming. Other hypotheses have been introduced to explain the action, but lack force by virtue of their arbitrary nature. Einstein, however, was able to show from the general considerations of the complete relativity theory that all planetary orbits should possess an almost infinitesimal rotation in the same direction as the planet moves. For the outer planets the effect is so small as to escape detection. Proximity to the gravitational field of the sun, however, intensifies the action. For Mercury, the innermost of the planets, calculation gives forty-three seconds of arc per century, a result in good accord with the average of observed values.

CURVATURE OF LIGHT IN THE SUN'S GRAVITATIONAL FIELD

The last deduction of the relativity theory which we shall treat in this chapter is the curvature of light in a gravitational field. When discussing the accelerated room in free space it was shown that this effect should be expected. (See pages 59-61 and Figure 8.) Even from the point of view, established under the Special Theory, that light, energy, and mass are convertible one into the other, we might suspect that energy should possess some of the properties of mass. The detection of this action seems like the most conclusive evidence in favor of Einstein's work, since it had not previously been suspected nor did it form part of the fundamental hypothesis.

Einstein predicted that the action of the sun's gravitational

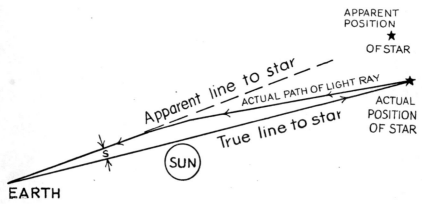

Fig. 12—APPARENT DISPLACEMENT OF STAR LYING CLOSE TO A LINE THROUGH SUN'S EDGE

field was sufficient to produce a deflection of 1.7 seconds of arc in a light beam, provided it passed almost tangent to the sun's surface. (See Figure 12.) The action is qualitatively the same as that on celestial bodies coming within the sun's field; the difference being due to the enormous speed of light. A body drifting at slow speed (less than twenty miles per second) would fall directly into the sun, as is the case with a meteor. For a body whose speed was about twenty miles per second (at 100,000,000 miles distant) the gravitational action would not be sufficient to pull the body into the sun but only to deflect it constantly from its original path, thereby making it describe a circle. For a slightly higher velocity the circle becomes an ellipse. The planets belong in this class, although the divergence from the circle is very small. If the velocity increases to 28.284 miles per second at the given distance the orbit becomes a parabola;—a condition nearly satisfied by certain comets. Velocities higher than this lead to hyperbolic paths, the limiting case being a straight line. However, the limit would only be attained at infinite velocity, were this possible. So that even for the enormous velocity of light there would be a slight curving of the path.

It is a great tribute to the lack of national prejudice among

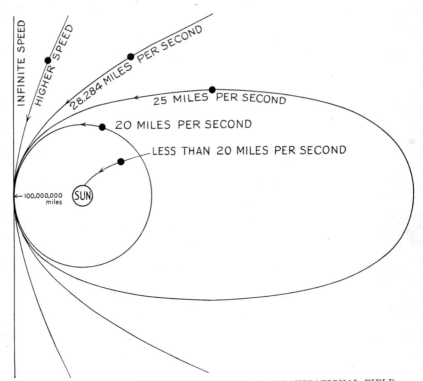

Fig. 13—CURVATURE OF LIGHT IN THE SUN'S GRAVITATIONAL FIELD

scientists, that it was a group of English astronomers who first checked Einstein's predictions in regard to the curvature of light. At the time of the solar eclipse of May 29, 1919, the Royal Society and the Royal Astronomical Society fitted out expeditions to Sobral in Brazil and Principe in West Africa, despite the material and psychological disorganization incident to the aftermath of the World War. The conditions of total eclipse were necessary for the test since otherwise the great luminosity of the sun's disk would blot out any star appearing close to its edge. The difficulties encountered even at the time of a total eclipse may be appreciated from the fact that the anticipated discrepancies in the star positions amounted to only a few hundredths of a millimeter on the photographic plates. Furthermore, the sudden change of temperature incident to the eclipse renders the accurate adjustment of astronomical instruments very difficult.

Careful analysis of the photographs made by these two expeditions gave good agreement with Einstein's calculations. The general theory of relativity had been vindicated, but it must not be supposed that universal acceptance followed. A great many astronomers felt that the observational errors were more than sufficient to explain any deviations found by the British expeditions; nor was it inconceivable that temperature variations might have led to the displacements recorded.

In 1922 the Lick Observatory sent an expedition to study the Australian eclipse. Every possible precaution suggested by the criticism given to former measurements was taken. The agreement between prediction and observation was even closer. A deviation of 1.72 seconds was obtained where the Einstein calculation gave 1.75 seconds. Surely this is conclusive evidence in favor of the general theory of relativity.

❦   ❦   ❦

OUTSTANDING FACTS FROM CHAPTER IV

1. When bodies or systems are moving in straight lines and at uniform speeds, Einstein's *special* theory of relativity states that a natural law holds equally well for any system. Einstein's *general* theory of relativity extended the principle to systems moving with accelerated speeds and in paths other than straight.
2. The acceleration of a body when acted upon by a direct push or pull is easily understandable, but the acceleration of a body caused by gravitation is not so easily understood; for if we assume that all acceleration is caused by a force, this, in the case of gravitation, means a force is acting at a distance—that is, without any contact with the body. This necessitated the idea of an ether. Einstein's theory of curved space, however, does away with the necessity for an ether.
3. Light rays when passing through a gravitational field are slightly de-

flected. The deflection is slight because of the extreme velocity of light. This seems to be at variance with the fundamental concept of relativity—that the velocity of light in a vacuum remains constant— but Einstein, claiming that the laws of nature are invariable, states that only in regions free from gravitational influence does the velocity of light remain fixed, *i.e.,* the constancy of the velocity of light is not a *natural law.*

4. The three dimensions in classical geometry are length, breadth, and thickness. A curved surface is readily understandable and capable of measurement by reference to the third dimension. A description of curved *space,* on the other hand, requires a reference to the fourth dimension, which, while it can be demonstrated mathematically, cannot be represented visually to beings like ourselves thinking in but three dimensions.

5. According to the Newtonian theory, a center of the universe would exist where the average density of matter is greatest. Going outward from this region the stars would therefore become fewer in number— suggesting a finite universe. Astronomical evidence disagrees with such a condition, showing that there is no diminishing of stars in any one direction. The curvature of gravitational space in the general theory of relativity yields the possible solution to the problem.

6. In curved space, a straight line is of finite length; that is, a line of unimpeded sight would return to the back of our head. The length of the circuit would be the circumference of the universe, calculated to be some 400,000,000 light years.

7. The two most important proofs of the Einstein theory of relativity are connected with:
   a. The displacement of the perihelion of Mercury's orbit, and
   b. The curvature of light passing near the sun's disk.
      (1) A perihelion is that point in an orbit nearest the sun. In calculating the shifting of the perihelion of Mercury's orbit, Einstein's formulas account for all the shifting very exactly.
      (2) It has been previously stated that light will curve when passing through a gravitational field. Einstein predicted that the gravitational field of the sun was capable of deflecting a light beam (almost tangent to the sun's surface) 1.7 seconds of an arc. Later experiments proved this to be so.

CHAPTER V

EINSTEIN'S FIFTH PAPER

THE AIM OF SCIENCE

IT IS ever the aim of science to reduce the complexity of the phenomena around us through the discovery of fundamental laws, such laws as will lend themselves to the description of two or more phenomena. Through such relationships, we simplify, in our own minds, the complexity that is presented to us by nature. The ultimate aim of science, according to what has just been said, would be to develop a single law, perhaps expressed by an equation, which would underlie every phenomenon of nature.

Toward this end scientists have been working for centuries with remarkable success. It was a great achievement when Newton was able to explain the great mysteries of the motion of the planets of the solar system in terms of so simple a thing as the manner in which an apple might be observed to fall to the ground. What for many years had seemed to man a very mysterious thing was explained in terms of a very simple mechanical experiment. It was the first great accomplishment in the chain of *unification of all natural phenomena into one simple whole*. Newton aimed farther, he tried to unify the laws of gravitation with those of light. In this he failed. The beautiful and exact experimental verification which supported the wave theory of light led to the complete abandonment of his corpuscular theory. Today the quantum (or "bundle") theory, which in many respects resembles the corpuscular theory of Newton, vies with the wave theory for acceptance. We are not so sure how the race will come out. The present is one of great confusion.

But, whatever the nature of light, it has nevertheless been shown that all forms of radiation are of the same nature. This much science, following its usual course of unification, has achieved. Such phenomena as cosmic rays, x-rays, gamma rays from radium, ultra-violet rays, visible light, heat radiation, and the electromagnetic waves of the broadcasting station, have all been brought under the same category. They are, in general, merely the same kind of ether disturbance but they are of various wave lengths.

Electricity and magnetism have long been interrelated. The one frequently appears as the accompaniment of the other. The equations of Clerk Maxwell related these two with the phenomenon of radiation. Clerk Maxwell showed that light was composed of two disturbances at right angles to each other, an electric and a magnetic, which were propagated through the ether. It remained for Hertz to show how such disturbances could be created by means of electrical apparatus—the foundation of modern radio broadcasting.

EINSTEIN'S CONTRIBUTIONS TO UNIFICATION OF PHENOMENA

As has been seen from what has gone before in this book, great credit for the unification of various phenomena known to us must go to Einstein and his theory of relativity. Whereas electricity and magnetism appeared definitely to be related, it remained for the special theory to show that the same set of equations which expressed one of these phenomena in one set of co-ordinates, expresses the other, at the same time, in another set of co-ordinates. We have found, in the theory of relativity, an explanation for the change of mass which had been found to occur with velocity of a moving charged particle and we have arrived from this at the conclusion that all mass must be regarded as electromagnetic in its nature.

In the case of the general theory of relativity we have found other valuable correlations. We have found that gravity, itself, could be explained in terms of mechanical motion. We have found that all the effects, which we attribute to a mysterious something called gravitation, can be very simply explained in terms of an accelerated body. The terms velocity, acceleration, and gravity, have taken on a new meaning for us—a meaning which, once understood, simplifies our whole concept of these terms.

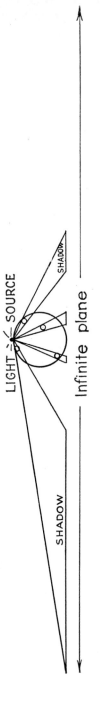

LIGHT SOURCE

SHADOW

SHADOW

Infinite plane

UNBOUNDED THOUGH FINITE SPACE

If space is unbounded it is difficult to understand what can be meant by saying that it can be finite in spite of this. The word finite means that it can be bounded very definitely. Are we not using an impossible contradiction of terms?

Suppose we have a plane which is infinite in extent in all directions. Now suppose we place upon this plane a large glass sphere and on top of it place a strong light source. Now suppose we allow the surface of this sphere to be inhabited by creatures who are opaque and who cast shadows upon the plane. As the individuals go about their daily lives on the surface of the sphere their every action is being followed by their shadows on the infinite plane. If we could see only the shadows and their behavior we might think that the shadows were endowed with intelligence. They would behave so rationally that it would be

hard for us to believe that they were but shadows of rational creatures inhabiting a sphere which we do not see.

Now as these beings on the sphere go nearer and nearer the top of the sphere their shadows go farther and farther out from the sphere. If one were right at the top its shadow would be at an infinite distance from the sphere. The shadow would, at the same time, become infinitely large, for the closer the individual is to the light the larger the shadow. Since at the same time as the shadows move toward infinity they become correspondingly large they would find no more room to move around in than they previously had, and it would be impossible for them to form any conception of infinite space. Their world is infinite but it is bounded by their very nature, inasmuch as they are shadows of beings on a finite world. Their space is unbounded though finite.

79

In addition to these things the general theory leads to some interesting results as regards light. It has been shown that light behaves as if it had mass. This has been proven experimentally, as already described, by observation of the path of light passing close to the sun. Thus the general theory has done what Newton set out to do—related gravitation with light. It has not, however, given us a single set of equations for the two phenomena descriptive of both by transferring to a different co-ordinate system. To do so required a still further extension of the mathematical system employed, a thing which makes it necessary for us to make a slight halt while we review our geometry.

Euclidean Geometry

Doubtless every one will recall some of the simple things of geometry learned at school. We accepted, as axioms, such things as that a straight line is the shortest distance between two points, that parallel lines were those which never meet no matter how far they may be extended, that the sum of the three angles of a triangle always equals 180 degrees. These facts, which belong to the system of geometry known as Euclidean geometry, were never questioned. If we were to find that any one of them were untrue then the whole system of Euclidean geomtry would be broken down. Any system which might develop under such circumstances would lead to entirely different results, for the most part, than those to which we are accustomed.

In general, Euclidean geometry applies to a plane. This, however, is not necessarily the case. If we take a piece of paper and draw upon it various figures to illustrate the fundamental axioms of Euclidean geometry—triangles, parallel lines, and so on—and then bend this paper around to form a cone, the laws which we have built up will still hold. We shall still find that the parallel lines will never meet, except possibly where they may cross at the edge of the paper. This form of meeting is not in accordance with our meaning, however. We shall still find that the angles of the triangle make 180 degrees; that the straight line is still the shortest distance between two points so

INFINITE THOUGH BOUNDED SPACE

When we think of the infinite we are accustomed to think of something that goes on and on without end. No matter how far we may go toward the infinite we have not decreased our distance from it one whit. To speak of space which is infinite though bounded would, on this basis, appear to be a contradiction of terms. The very instant we place a boundary on our space it would seem that it must cease to be infinite.

It is necessary to explain what we mean by the phrase, "infinite though bounded." A very good definition has been given by the mathematician, Poincaré. Briefly it is as follows. Suppose we have a great circular

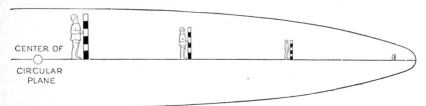

CENTER OF
CIRCULAR
PLANE

plane which constitutes the universe for a certain race of beings. Suppose, farther, that as these individuals proceed toward the edge of their universe they gradually shrink in size, as does every object in this strange universe.

Suppose now, equipped with measuring rods, these individuals start to measure their universe, proceeding from the center toward the edge. As they go farther and farther from the center their measuring rods get shorter and shorter. They, themselves, are proportionately decreased in size and, since everything else is changed in the same way, nothing unusual is noticed. Their steps get shorter and shorter. Eventually they become infinitely small, take infinitely short steps, and measure with infinitely short measuring rods. Of course they never reach the end of their universe.

They must, then, assume that their universe is infinite in extent or that they themselves shrink as has just been described. This latter possibility would appear as absurd to them as a suggestion that the earth and everything on it were shrinking would appear to you. It is easier for them to believe that their universe is infinite in extent.

Yet looked at by a superior being they are on a large flat plane with sharp boundaries. Because they cannot reach these boundaries they do not believe that boundaries exist. Their plane is infinite in one sense though it is bounded in another sense. It is infinite though bounded. Space appears to us infinite. Is it?

long as we remain on the surface of the paper. In other words, our Euclidean geometry, with slight changes in the meaning of a few terms, still holds.

But suppose we draw all the figures referred to on some material that will stretch, and suppose, having drawn them, we proceed to cover a sphere with the elastic sheet. We shall find that it will not cover the sphere smoothly unless it is stretched. When we stretch it something must happen to our figures. We may find that our parallel lines converge; we may find that the three angles of our triangle now equal more than 180 degrees. In short, we ruined our whole system of geometry the instant we began to stretch the material.

We must start all over again and invent new axioms. When we have done so we have invented a system of spherical geometry. In this system the shortest distance between two points is the distance along a great circle passing through the two points. We shall find that there are always more than 180 degrees in the three angles of a triangle. We shall still have a system of geometry, but it will not be the Euclidean geometry. We shall find it useful when we are dealing with spherical surfaces.

Plane geometry was developed by the Egyptians. Every year it was necessary for them to resurvey the land along the Nile because of the periodical floods. It was necessary for them to lay down some simple rules to go by in order that they could accomplish this task in a minimum time. Plane geometry was the result. But it may occur to you that the earth is not a plane surface but rather a spherical one. Why was it not necessary for them to use the laws of spherical geometry? Because the area over which they surveyed was so small that the curvature of the earth did not become noticeable. Had they attempted to survey over a large enough area they would have found that the three angles of a triangle totaled more than 180 degrees. Had this fact been barely noticeable they would have attributed it to an error in their measurements. Since they did not know that the earth was round it is quite unlikely that this would have occurred to them. Their belief in a flat earth would have been too thoroughly ingrained to have led them to believe that the earth was round rather than to believe that they themselves had made an error. Perhaps we are in very much the same condition now. We have not thought of space as having any definite shape or boundaries. We find it hard to obtain a mental picture of curved space, or of finite, though unbounded, space. The fault may be with our habits of thinking.

NON-EUCLIDEAN GEOMETRY

But suppose we go on to a still different geometry. Suppose we find that our interest is in some such solid figure as an ellipsoid, something of about the shape of a door-knob, or possibly the shape of a rugby football. This will lead to a geometry both non-Euclidean and non-spherical. For this we shall have to invent a wholly new geometry. Such a geometry has been worked out by Riemann. He has worked out a perfectly general geometry applicable to all surfaces, a geometry of which spherical geometry is but a special case. It is a geometry of which it is true that it becomes the same as Euclidean geometry if we consider only an infinitely small area of the surface. The instant we consider definite areas, Euclidean geometry no longer holds. In this geometry it is impossible to say that two lines, which are a finite distance apart, are parallel. If we move a line parallel to itself continuously it may not have the same direction when any point on it has returned to its original position.

If one again reviews the special theory of relativity it will be seen that what has been done is very simple insofar as geometry is concerned. Einstein has merely used the three-dimensional Euclidean system enriched by the introduction of a fourth dimension—time. In the case of the general theory he has found it necessary to resort to the Riemannian geometry.

THE UNIFORM-FIELD EQUATIONS

So far, Einstein has invented no new tools to work with. He has used those geometries that were at hand which suited his purpose. Such was not the case, however, in his uniform-field theory. Here he may well be said to have invented a new geometry for his purpose. This geometry is like true Euclidean

geometry in that it permits of lines at a distance being parallel
—distant parallelism. It is like the Riemannian in that if one
line passes across two parallel lines, a line parallel to the first
does not necessarily do so. Einstein, writing in the New York
Times, is very clear on this point. He says:

"The new uniform-field theory is based on the following
mathematical discovery: There are continua with a Riemannian
matrix and distant parallelism which nevertheless are not
Euclidean. It is easy to show, for instance, in the case of
three-dimensional space, how such a continuum differs from a
Euclidean.

"First of all, in such a continuum there are lines whose elements are parallel to one an-
other. We shall call these
'straight lines.' It also has a
definite meaning to speak of
two parallel straight lines as
in the Euclidean case. Now
choose two such parallel lines
E_1L_1 and E_2L_2 and mark on

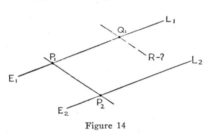

Figure 14

each a point, P_1 and P_2. (See Fig. 14.)

"On E_1L_1 choose in addition a point Q_1. If we now draw
through Q_1 a straight line, Q_1R, parallel to the straight line
P_1P_2, then in Euclidean geometry this will cut the straight line
E_2L_2; in the geometry now used the line Q_1R and the line E_2L_2
do not in general cut one another. To this extent the geometry
now used is not only a specialization of the Riemannian, but
also a generalization of the Euclidean geometry. My opinion
is that our space-time continuum has a structure of the kind here
outlined."

It was a study of such a continuum, applying to it the most
simple and natural conditions possible, that led to the uniform-
field equations for electromagnetism and gravitation first announced by Einstein in his so-called fifth paper given before the
Prussian Academy of Sciences, January 30, 1929. It was this
paper that attracted so much attention that newspapers throughout the world printed it as front-page news, and caused the New
York *Herald Tribune* to reproduce it in its entirety in the edition

following the reading of it before the Prussian Academy. It was cabled complete, which, considering its complexity, has been considered a feat in journalism seldom if ever equaled.

SIGNIFICANCE OF NEW FIELD EQUATIONS

Having set up equations which fit, alike, both the phenomena of electromagnetism and of gravitation, what has been gained? Does the expression show that these two phenomena are one and the same? The answer to this must be in the negative. It does not prove anything. It does suggest, however, an identity which we should be slow if we did not follow up. It is a clue of which we should try to make the most. If we were to come into a room, find a smoldering gun on the floor, and a clot of blood beside it, we should be less than intelligent if it did not occur to us that possibly a murder had been committed. We should be guilty of a real fault if we did not make an attempt to prove or disprove our suspicions. The same is true here. The uniform equations for the expression of the two phenomena suggest that they are but different manifestations of the same thing. We should expect next to prove or disprove this by studying special solutions of these equations to find whether or not they lead to results which we know to be in accord with experiment.

Perhaps the situation may be made clearer if we refer again to the relation between gravitation and acceleration found in the general theory of relativity (Chapter IV). Here it was shown that all the effects which we ascribe to gravitation could be duplicated in a body with a uniform acceleration. Gravitation, instead of being a force acting either at a distance or through some medium, became simply a manifestation of acceleration. The new uniform-field theory, which indicates that there is close relationship existing between gravitation and electromagnetism, may yet show us that the apparently mysterious forces of electricity and magnetism are nothing more than different manifestations of some other phenomenon which we have become accustomed to think simple. We are well on our way, then, toward reducing all phenomena to the point where they can be regarded simply as different manifestations of the same thing.

SOLUTION OF THE FIELD EQUATIONS

Since finding the uniform equations Einstein has been devoting himself to solutions for special cases. Naturally, as has already been pointed out, the equations will be valueless unless they are eventually found to fit the experimental facts. In order to put them to such a test it is necessary to find a solution for some simple case which has its counterpart in well known physical conditions. This Einstein did and presented his findings in a paper early in 1930. In this paper he gave the solutions for two special cases; first the case of an isolated sphere charged electrically; second, the case of a number of charged points in space. In each case it was considered that the mass was to be constant.

Let us now see why it was that Einstein chose these two particular cases for solution. Consider the first of these. How are we going to get a sphere charged and isolated from other objects? This requires no effort on our part for we have approximately this condition in two well known and much investigated cases. The first of these is the earth. For all practical purposes, provided it is charged, the earth fits the conditions set up by Einstein. The only question is as to whether or not it is charged. We usually regard it as at zero potential electrically. This would infer that it is not charged. The conclusion, however, is quite unjustified. When we say it is at zero potential we are merely saying that we are going to use it as a convenient reference point in potential measurements. In a similar way we use the level of the sea as our zero of level. It does not mean that there can be no place at a level lower than this. It merely means that it is a convenient level to use for purposes of other measurements. We can have levels below it as well as above, as every one knows. If we were outside the earth the earth might be to us a highly charged body. Astronomical investigations, should they fit in with the solutions found by Einstein, may prove to us that the earth is, in actual fact, highly charged. Perhaps here we may find some relations that may give us information concerning the northern lights; or perhaps we may learn something of the so-called Heaviside * layer, a layer high in the earth's atmosphere supposed to consist of highly ionized particles which cause reflections of radio waves.

But there is still another case where we may easily obtain a charged particle in an isolated condition. This is the electron. An electron does not have to be far from other particles to be outside of any influence from them. Whether or not it can be regarded as a sphere, however, is another question. In any case it would seem that an electron, isolated from its neighbors, might offer another means of testing Einstein's solution and, as a result, we might obtain some information about the electron itself.

The other solution, which has been worked out, again applies both to things of astronomical and atomic dimensions. The second solution, as has been said, applies to a number of charged points in space. Such a system is not unlike our universe, for while the parts of this system as we think of them are very large, viewed as a universe their size is very small as compared to their distances apart. For practical purposes they may be viewed as a collection of points. To fit Einstein's solution they must be charged points. Whether they are or are not we cannot say. It will only be proven so if future observations fit in with the solution found for the general field equation for this special case.

The condition of the second solution fits in also with what is known as a space charge. A space charge consists of a number of electrons, or of protons as the case may be, separated from each other and confined, for some reason, to a rather definite locality. Such space charges are made use of in the modern radio vacuum tube. Perhaps measurements on space charges might give us some clue as to the correctness of Einstein's uniform-field equation. Up to the time of writing there have been no experiments in confirmation of them. This does not mean that there will be none; such verification will undoubtedly require a considerable amount of very accurate work.

---

* Named for Oliver Heaviside.

Value of Einstein's Work

It has been frequently asked what practical significance are these results likely to have. This is a question impossible to answer. Obviously if any one could see any practical results at the present time they would soon be put into operation. Here we can only fall back on some old stories which show that in similar cases great things have come out of such theories. There is a story that Faraday, when asked what practical significance might result from his studies on the relations between electricity and magnetism, replied that perhaps a future generation might be able to tax them. This has indeed been so; for from his experiments came the whole mass of electromagnetic machinery that we have today. The huge electric generators which send out power over miles of wires to turn the wheels of our factories and to light our buildings would not be possible without Faraday's experiments.

What possible practical result could come from Maxwell's electromagnetic equations? Certainly at the time they were formulated one would have said, "Nothing." But with a Hertz to devise an experimental test of Maxwell's work and a Marconi to put this into practical form, we have modern radio-broadcasting.

Another example, equally cogent, is that of the photo-electric cell—a case in which Professor Einstein had a part. In 1887 Heinrich Hertz discovered that ultra-violet light had an effect on electrical discharge. Further study in this direction was made by Hallwachs, and the effect of light on discharge became known as the Hallwachs effect.

Very little progress was made in developing this new knowledge so that it might serve a useful purpose until 1905, at which time Einstein gave us the now famous Einstein photo-electric equation which relates the electric behavior to the wave length of the light used to produce the Hallwachs effect through the use of the quantum theory which was then in its infancy. The equation was quickly confirmed by Professor Millikan and others.

From then on the development of the photo-electric effect

to a useful stage has kept pace with the development of radio tubes which were necessary before the radio could be brought to full fruition. We now have all manner of photo-electric devices. They open doors when a beam of light is intercepted, they control traffic lights, they level elevators automatically, they match delicate colors with great speed and accuracy, they have

Fig. 15—OUR EARTH IS MOVING IN TIME AS WELL AS IN SPACE

given us talking motion-pictures and television. The photo-electric effect has given us a whole retinue of robots.

But we would be less than fair if we were to neglect to point out that Einstein's work has already been of immense practical benefit. We must not confine the use of the word *practical* to mean only those things which give us physical comfort or pleasure. Those things which affect us mentally are far deeper in their significance. Einstein has given us a new philosophy of life. He has caused us to raise our eyes from our mole-hill and to comprehend something of the great plan of the universe. His theories have been just as broadening to our mental outlook as was the discovery that the earth was not flat, but spherical. Einstein has added a deeper significance to our lives. In a single generation this man has made deeper strides into the mystery of our existence than have been made in all previous history. He is a mental giant, who, with kindly hand, carries us all forward with him in his easy stride.

The Future

And now, what next? No one, not even Einstein, can tell. He is like a man working on a puzzle. He patiently tries one part after another. Many have to be discarded; now one fits, and it is added to those which have already been built into a pattern. He knows not, nor does any one else, when he shall pick up a piece that will be the key to the whole picture; around which everything else will fit with ease. In the meantime he goes on working quietly and unostentatiously in his study with his pipe, or sailing hour after hour on the lake in front of his house, always writing down equations and more equations. To-morrow he may have a brilliant idea that will set the world buzzing. Or it may be just an ordinary day of minor accomplishment for one of Einstein's mental stature. Rest assured, however, there is more to come.

OUTSTANDING FACTS FROM CHAPTER V

1. The universal aim of science, as previously stated, is to reduce the complexity of natural phenomena through the discovery of a fundamental law which will apply to all phenomena. The discoveries of Newton were a great achievement in establishing such laws, making understandable much that before was clouded in mystery.
2. The general theory of relativity has explained:
   a. gravity in terms of mechanical motion,
   b. the effects of gravitation in terms of accelerated motions, and
   c. that light, like mass, is affected in a so-called gravitational field.
3. Euclidian, or classical, geometry, with its famous axioms—a straight line is the shortest distance between two points—parallel lines never meet—the sum of the interior angles of a triangle always equals 180° —holds good only in the case of plane surfaces. In dealing with surfaces of a sphere, a new geometry with new axioms had to be invented, i.e., a spherical geometry. In dealing with surfaces other than plane or spherical, still another geometry based on other axioms was necessary. Riemann worked out such a geometry applicable to all surfaces of which spherical geometry was a special case, and showed that the axioms of Euclidian geometry were true for only an infinitely small area of the surface. Einstein invented still another geometry upon

which his unifield-field theory is based; a theory, the equations of which fit alike the phenomena of both electromagnetism and gravitation.

4. The general theory indicates a strong resemblance between gravitation and electromagnetism, and may in time lead to the proof that the foregoing are nothing more than different manifestations of the same thing.

5. The question as to the practical value of Einstein's work may be compared to a question asked of Faraday concerning the practical advantages of his theories regarding the relationship of magnetism and electricity. Faraday said that a future generation might be able to tax them. Witness the development of applied electricity in the last fifty years!

LORENTZ TRANSFORMATIONS

THE mathematical expression which is evolved, if the law of the constant rate of transmission of light is used as a criterion and the two assumptions—the relativity of time and the relativity of distance—are permitted, is known as the Lorentz transformation. The form of transformation may be under-

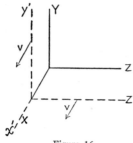

Figure 16

stood by a reference to Figure 16. Here the *unprimed axes* represent a stationary co-ordinate system; the *primed set*, one moving with a velocity v along the direction of x. In accordance with the restriction that a ray of light shall have the same velocity with respect to both the fixed and the moving system, we find that an event described by the co-ordinates x, y, z, and t (time axis not shown in figure since a four-dimensional system is not subject to diagrammatic representation) on the fixed system, is located at:

$$(a) \ x' = \frac{x - vt}{\sqrt{1 - \dfrac{v^2}{c^2}}} \qquad (b) \ y' = y \qquad (c) \ z' = z$$

$$(d) \ t' = \frac{t - \dfrac{vx}{c^2}}{\sqrt{1 - \dfrac{v^2}{c^2}}}$$

where x', y', z', and t' are the co-ordinates on the moving system. Here c is the velocity of light in a vacuum.

To show that the above transformation satisfies the impressed condition, imagine a light impulse traveling along the x direction. In the fixed system the location is then given by

$x = ct$. (Merely the expression distance equals velocity times time.) In the moving system, from the above relations, we have (substituting ct for x)

$$(1) \quad x' = \frac{ct - vt}{\sqrt{1 - \dfrac{v^2}{c^2}}} = \frac{(c - v)\, t}{\sqrt{1 - \dfrac{v^2}{c^2}}}$$

and (2)
$$t' = \frac{t - \dfrac{vct}{c^2}}{\sqrt{1 - \dfrac{v^2}{c^2}}} = \frac{\left(1 - \right)\dfrac{v}{c}\, t}{\sqrt{1 - \dfrac{v^2}{c^2}}}$$

Now dividing equation 1 by equation 2 gives

$$\frac{x'}{t'} = \frac{(c - v)\, t}{\left(1 - \dfrac{v}{c}\right) t} = c \text{ or } x' = ct'$$

which is the required relation for the velocity of propagation of light with respect to the moving axis at the velocity c. Although the direction of the light beam has in this instance for simplicity been restricted to the x axis, the same result would be obtained no matter what direction were chosen.

Looking back at the Lorentz transformations one notes that (a) gives the change in length predicted by Fitzgerald and Lorentz. For example with the case given, a yardstick placed along the axis in the moving system would have a length equal to $\sqrt{1 - \dfrac{v^2}{c^2}}$ times one yard, as measured from the system at rest. Albeit if measured by a foot rule in the moving system it would still contain three foot lengths, for the foot rule would have shrunk in like proportion. Hence to any one in the moving system the shrinkage is imperceptible; or to be more correct, does not exist. From (b) we see that a device which would tick seconds in the stationary system, if placed in the moving one and timed from an outside stationary point, would give impulses $\dfrac{1}{\sqrt{1 - \dfrac{v^2}{c^2}}}$ seconds in length.

ENERGY-MASS RELATIONS

$\mathbf{I}$ N NEWTONIAN mechanics the energy possessed by a body of mass m moving with a velocity v, and devoid of rotation, is given by $\frac{mv^2}{2}$. This is called the kinetic energy of translation. In the relativity mechanics this becomes $\dfrac{mc^2}{\sqrt{1 - \dfrac{v^2}{c^2}}}$. We note, however, from the last expression that even were the mass at rest $(v = 0)$ it would still possess a kinetic energy equal to mc^2, $\left(\dfrac{mc^2}{\sqrt{1 - 0}}\right) = mc^2$. The apparent contradiction here we will leave for a moment. Regarding the other limit, when $v = c$, it follows that the energy would be infinite.

If the expression $\dfrac{mc^2}{\sqrt{1 - \dfrac{v^2}{c^2}}}$ be written as $mc^2 \left(1 - \dfrac{v^2}{c^2}\right)^{-\frac{1}{2}}$ the binomial expansion may be applied, giving: $mc^2 + \dfrac{mv^2}{2} + \dfrac{3}{8} m \dfrac{v^4}{c^2} + \ldots$ Now for the cases usually treated in mechanics, where v is small in comparison to c, the third and higher terms become insignificant; so that when the stationary energy value mc^2 is subtracted, we have the Newtonian expression $\dfrac{mv^2}{2}$. This reduction of the general relativity expression to the common classical form for all but exceptional cases is typical of all quantities treated.

This change of mass as measured on the stationary basis discussed above, you will recall, agrees with the experimental evidence found. This was done by Kaufmann, when working with high speed electrons, four years previous to the announcement of the relativity theory (see Chapter II). A change of mass was due to the velocity effect alone, but another influence may alter initial mass. Einstein expresses the relation in an interesting form by employing the electrodynamical equations of Clerk Maxwell. Assuming a body to be moving with a velocity v and to absorb energy in an amount E, measured with respect to the moving axes, then the increase in energy of the body measured with respect to a stationary set of axes would be $\dfrac{E}{\sqrt{1-\dfrac{v^2}{c^2}}}$.

Hence the total energy would be the initial energy, $\dfrac{mc^2}{\sqrt{1-\dfrac{c^2}{v^2}}}$

(as given above) plus the increase, $\dfrac{E}{\sqrt{1-\dfrac{v^2}{c^2}}}$ or $\dfrac{\left(m+\dfrac{E}{c^2}\right)c^2}{\sqrt{1-\dfrac{v^2}{c^2}}}$.

This appears exactly the same as the kinetic energy of inertial mass $\left(m+\dfrac{E}{c^2}\right)$ whose velocity is v. In other words by absorbing the amount of energy E, the inertial mass has increased by the amount $\dfrac{E}{c^2}$, i.e., energy has disappeared and mass appeared in its place.

Since the energy absorbed is usually in the form of radiation, the inclusion of Planck's formula, energy equals Planck's constant times frequency of radiation ($E = h v$), proves helpful. We may now say that the conversion relation, $m = \dfrac{hv}{c^2}$, holds for the transformation of radiant energy into mass, or vice versa.

SUGGESTIONS FOR FURTHER READING

Prepared by the Author

ORIGIN, NATURE, AND INFLUENCE OF RELATIVITY—*George David Birkhoff*
MACMILLAN
The book is written primarily for the non-mathematical reader and the mathematical formulas are limited to two chapters. The untrained man will find it sometimes difficult to follow.

COSMIC EVOLUTION—*John Elof Boodin*
MACMILLAN
A discussion of cosmogony, evolution, and man. About a third of the book is given to the relativity doctrine. A well written, scholarly book.

SPACE AND TIME—*Emile Borel*
BLACKIE
This is a clear exposition for the general reader, but lacks the more recent phases of the problem.

RISE OF MODERN PHYSICS—*Henry Crew*
WILLIAMS
Prepared for the general reader, who will find much of interest, but there are many passages too difficult to understand without special training in physics.

EVOLUTION OF SCIENTIFIC THOUGHT FROM NEWTON TO EINSTEIN
—*A. D'Abro*
BONI
The scope of the book is indicated in its title—a review of the evolution of scientific thought and achievement resulting finally in the Einstein theory of relativity.

NATURE OF THE PHYSICAL WORLD—*Arthur Stanley Eddington*
MACMILLAN
An exposition of the leading ideas of modern physics written with all the clarity and charm of this distinguished author. Not always easy to follow, but always interesting.

RELATIVITY—*Albert Einstein* (translated)
HOLT
Has the advantage of the master's touch. Contains some mathematical treatments which may be omitted without too much loss of clarity.

EINSTEIN THEORY EXPLAINED AND ANALYZED—*Samuel H. Guggenheimer*
MACMILLAN
A conservative but fair summary of the basic assumptions of the Einstein theory. Written for those with some scientific and philosophic foundation.

FROM NEWTON TO EINSTEIN—*Benjamin Harrow*
VAN NOSTRAND
This is written in a popular style and is rich in references to more complete works.

RELATIVITY—*Sir Oliver Joseph Lodge*
DOUBLEDAY
A brief and simple presentation of a difficult subject, showing its significance in human thought.

TYRANNY OF TIME: EINSTEIN OR BORGSON?—*Charles Nordmann*, translated from the French by *E. E. Fournier d'Albe*
INT. PUB.
An interesting and informing discussion of time and relativity.

GRAVITATION VS. RELATIVITY—*Charles Lane Poor*
PUTNAM
A review of astronomical measurements to show the difficult nature of interpreting the small variations from Newton's laws so far found. Interesting as a strong support for Newtonian mechanics.

A B C OF RELATIVITY—*Bertrand Arthur William Russell*
HARPER
An excellent little book by a writer who has the happy faculty of making difficult subjects plain and interesting to the lay reader.

RELATIVITY AND THE UNIVERSE—*Henry Schmidt* (translated)
McBRIDE
A brief non-mathematical discussion.

FOUR LECTURES ON RELATIVITY AND SPACE—*Charles Steinmetz* McGRAW-HILL
Quite mathematical in spots, but rich in examples which clarify the problem.

THREE MEN DISCUSS RELATIVITY—*John William Navin Sullivan*
KNOPF
Explaining the Einstein theory to the layman by way of the conversational method—a discussion participated in by "a mathematical physicist, a philosopher, and an ordinary intelligent person."

96

KEY TO PUBLISHERS

BLACKIE—Blackie & Son, Ltd., 17 Stanhope Street, Glasgow, Scotland.
BONI—Boni & Liveright, Inc., 29 West 47th Street, New York, N. Y.
DOUBLEDAY—Doubleday, Doran & Company, Garden City, N. Y.
HARPER—Harper & Brothers, 49 East 33rd Street, New York, N. Y.
HOLT—Henry Holt & Company, Inc., 1 Park Avenue, New York, N. Y.
INT. PUB.—International Publishers Co., Inc., 381 Fourth Avenue, New York, N. Y.
KNOPF—Alfred A. Knopf, 730 Fifth Avenue, New York, N. Y.
McBRIDE—Robert M. McBride & Company, 7 West 16th Street, New York, N. Y.
McGRAW-HILL—McGraw-Hill Book Company, 370 Seventh Avenue, New York, N. Y.
MACMILLAN—The Macmillan Co., 60 Fifth Avenue, New York, N. Y.
PUTNAM—G. P. Putnam's Sons, 2-6 West 45th Street, New York, N. Y.
VAN NOSTRAND—D. Van Nostrand Company, 250 Fourth Avenue, New York, N. Y.
WILLIAMS—Williams & Wilkins Company, Mt. Royal and Guilford Avenues, Baltimore, Md.

GLOSSARY

[Only those terms are defined in this glossary which either are not explained in the text or are explained once and are used again several pages away from the explanation.]

APHELION: (from two Greek words, meaning "away from the sun"), the point of the orbit of a planet or a comet farthest from the sun.

ATOMIC THEORY OF NIELS BOHR: a description of an atom in terms of a massive central portion, called the nucleus, and surrounding or orbital electrons. The picture is made to agree with the evidence obtained by the spectroscope in analyzing the light from atoms excited by the passage of electricity, as in a neon sign tube, or by other means.

BETA PARTICLES: electrons shot from the core or nucleus of radio-active substances, such as radium, polonium, etc.

BROWNIAN MOVEMENTS: the peculiar rapid vibratory movement exhibited by the microscopic particles of both organic and inorganic substances when suspended in water or other fluids, so called from Dr. Robert Brown (1773-1858) who first demonstrated the commonness of the movement.

CONTINUUM: that which is absolutely continuous and selfsame.

CO-ORDINATE: any of two or more magnitudes that determine position, especially of spatial elements.

CORPUSCULAR THEORY OF LIGHT: this theory, enunciated by Sir Isaac Newton, is that light consists in the emission and rapid progression of minute particles or corpuscles.

ELECTRON: the smallest particle of negative electricity.

ELLIPSE: (1) the path of a point, the sum of whose distances from two fixed points (the foci) is constant; (2) a conic section made by a cutting plane whose angle with the base is less than that of the side element of the cone.

ENTROPY: a measure of the inavailability of energy. All natural changes tend to increase the entropy of a system, i.e., to make its energy less available.

HYPERBOLA: a curve formed by a section of a cone, when the cutting plane makes a greater angle with the base than that made by the side element of the cone.

KILOWATT HOUR: a unit of work or energy equal to that done by one thousand watts acting for one hour.

MACROSCOPIC BODIES: bodies large enough to be observed by the naked eye.

MAGNETO-OPTICS: a branch of physics dealing with the influence of the magnetic field upon light.

MASS: that property of a body to which its inertia is ascribed and which is commonly taken as the measure of the amount of material which it contains. Weight varies with locality, but mass is the same at all places.

MUTATION: a sudden heritable change in some aspect of the organism, due to an alteration in the hereditary material. Frequently in the restricted sense of a sudden change in a gene. (See "Heredity and Variation" in this Series.)

PARABOLA: (1) a curve, any point of which is equidistant from a fixed point, the focus, and from a fixed straight line; (2) a conic section made by a cutting plane which is parallel to the side element of the cone.

PERIHELION: (from two Greek words meaning "near the sun"), the point of the orbit of a planet or a comet nearest the sun.

PHOTO-ELECTRICITY: electricity produced by light.

QUANTUM THEORY: the theory that radiation from a body is emitted only in discrete units (called quanta), and that absorption occurs in the same discontinuous manner.

Radio-activity: the spontaneous emission by an element of rays consisting of material particles traveling at high velocities.

Refraction: the deflection from a straight path suffered by a ray of light, of heat, or of sound in passing obliquely from one medium into another in which its velocity is different, as for example from air into water.

Sport: in biology, a sudden spontaneous deviation or variation from type, which is unexplainable. (See "Heredity and Variation" in this *Series*.)

Vector: the symbol of a definite translation from one point to another in space; a means of representing any physical quantity which has directional properties.

Watt: a unit of power, equal to the rate of work represented by a current of one ampere under a pressure of one volt. An English horsepower is approximately equal to 746 watts.

INDEX
WITH PRONUNCIATIONS †

Accelerated system, 56, 58, 60*
Adams, John Couch (1819-1892), English astronomer: predicts Neptune, 25
Aphelion (à-fēl'yŭn): speculations of Newton, 21
Aristotle (ăr'ĭs-tŏt'''l) (384-322 B.C.), a Greek philosopher: teachings of, 16
Astrophysics: used to verify Einstein's theories, 51
Atoms: construction of, 52; quantum theory, 26
Bacon, Roger (1214?-1294), English philosopher, 18
Blood: color affected by heat, 24
Bohr (bōr), Niels (1885-), Danish physicist: atomic theory of, 26
Bomb dropped from plane, 41
Brownian movements, 6, 26
Cartesian (kär-tē'zhăn) co-ordinates, 36
Conservation of energy: Einstein's generalization re, 47; theory of, 22
Contraction theory, 31, 40, 46, 62
Conversion factor between mass and energy, 47
Co-ordinate system: time an element, 44
Co-ordinates, 35, 36
Corpuscular theory of light, 22, 29
Cosmic rays: origin of, 52
Curvature of light, 61, 71, 73*, 74*
Curved space, 63, 67, 69
Davy, Sir Humphry (1778-1829), an English chemist: experiments to prove conservation of energy, 24
Descartes (dā'kärt'), René (1596-1650), French philosopher and mathematician, 36
Direction: relativity of, 7
Distance: relativity of, 45
Duration: a dimension, 23
Earth: motion of, 9*; orbit calculated by Kepler, 18; relativity of past, present, and future, 27; relativity of time on, 11

Eddington, Arthur Stanley (1882-), English astronomer: explains long life of sun, 29
Einstein (īn'stīn), Albert (1879-), German physicist: biographical sketch, 8; criticises theory of Fitzgerald and Lorentz, 40; difficult to understand, 1; explains movement of Mercury's orbit, 72; extends quantum theory, 26; fifth paper, 3, 5*, 77; generalizations re conservation of energy, 47; his 1905 paper, 42; hobbies, 10; predicts amount of curvature of light in sun's gravitational field, 73; the man and the scientist, 4; value of his work, 88; *frontispiece*
Einstein riot, 3
Electric force, 57
Electron energy, 31, 50
Energy: conservation of, 22; Einstein's generalizations, 47; laws of thermodynamics, 24, 28; not independent of mass, 51; potential vs. rest, 47; quantum theory, 26; radioactivity, 28
Energy-mass relation equations, 94
Epicurus (ĕp''ĭ-kū'rŭs) (342?-270 B.C.), Greek philosopher: teachings of, 16
Equations, Uniform-field, 83
Ether, The: importance of, 29
Ether-drag, 30, 48
Euclidean (ū-klĭd'ĭ-ăn) geometry, 80
Falling bodies, Law of, 19
Field intensity, 58
First Law of Thermodynamics, 24, 28
Fitzgerald, George Francis (1851-1901), British physicist: contraction theory, 30, 40, 46
Fizeau (fē''zō'), Armande Hippolyte Louis (1819-1896), French physicist: experiments of, 30, 48, 50
Future, present, and past: relativity of, 27, 45, 49
Galaxies: number and speeds of, 70
Galileo Galilei (gä''lĕ-lā'ō, or găl''ĭ-lē'ō, gä''lĕ-lā'ē) (1564-1642), Italian astronomer, 18, 19

† For key to pronunciation, see page 104.
* Asterisk denotes illustration.

Galle (gäl'ē), Johann Gottfried (1812-1910), German astronomer: discovers Neptune, 25
Gauss (gous), Karl Friedrich (1777-1855), German mathematician: coordinates of, 66
General theory of relativity, 55
Geometry, Euclidean, 80
Geometry, Riemannian, 83
Geometry, Spherical, 82
Gravitation, 20
Gravitational Field: behavior of light, 59, 72, 73*, 74*; intensity of, 58
Hallwachs (häl'wäks), Wilhelm L. F. (1859-1922), German physicist, 88
Heat: conservation of energy, 24
Heaviside layer, 87
Helium atom: composition of, 52
Heraclitus (hĕr"ä-klī'tŭs) (fl. 500 B.C.), Greek philosopher: quoted, 15, 37
Hertz (hĕrts), Heinrich (1857-1894), German physicist: demonstrates existence of waves from oscillating electric current, 24; value of his work, 78, 88
Hubble, Edwin Powell (1889-   ), American astronomer: quoted, 70
Huygens (hī'genz or hoi'gĕns), Christian (1629-1695), Dutch physicist: contributions of, 19
Hydrogen: formed from radiation, 52
Inertia: Newton's theory, 21
Interference patterns, 30
Joule (joul), James Prescott (1818-1889), English physicist: establishes relation between heat and mechanical work, 24
Kaufmann (kouf'män), Walter (1871-   ), German physicist: discovers velocity changes mass of electrons, 31, 47, 50
Kepler (kĕp'lēr), Johann (1571-1630), German astronomer: laws of, 18
Kinetic theory, 6
Lagrange (lä'gränzh'), Joseph Louis, Comte (1736-1813), French mathematician: controversy with Laplace, 25
Laplace (lä"pläs'), Pierre Simon, Marquis de (1749-1827), French astronomer and mathematician: controversy with Lagrange, 25
Laws of Nature are universal, 42
Laws of Thermodynamics: first, 24, 28; second, 28
Length: change in, 31; relativity of, 44
Leverrier (lē-vĕ"ryä'), Urbain Jean Joseph (1811-1877), French astronomer: discovers movement of Mercury's orbit, 25, 72; predicts Neptune, 25

Light: behavior in a gravitational field, 59; curvature of, 61, 71, 73*, 74*; Newton's corpuscular theory, 29; velocity acts as a limiting value, 31; velocity in a vacuum, 42; velocity in various moving fluids, 30, 48; velocity of, a conversion factor between mass and energy, 47; velocity of, proof of Einstein's theory, 48; velocity varies, 61
Limiting value, 31
Location: defined, 35
Lorentz (lō'rĕnts), Hendrick Antoon (1853-   ), Dutch physicist: contraction theory, 30, 40, 46, 50; transformations, 92
Lucretius (lŭ-krē'shǐ-ŭs) (Titus Lucretius Caius) (96?-55 B.C.), Roman poet: theories of, 16
McLennan, John Cunningham (1867-   ), Canadian physicist: notices cosmic rays, 52
Magnetic force, 57
Marconi (mär-kō'nē), Guglielmo (1874-   ), Italian electrician: value of his work, 88
Mass: changed by velocity, 31, 32*, 47; Newton's law, 22; not independent of energy, 51
Mass-energy relation equations, 94
Maxwell, James Clerk (1831-1879), English physicist: his electromagnetic theory, 24; the ether hypothesis, 29; value of his work, 78, 88
Mayer, Julius Robert von (1814-1878), German physician: his theory of conservation of energy, 24
Measurement: relativity of, 17
Mercury: perihelion movement of, 25, 71, 72*
Michelson, Albert Abraham (1852-1931), German-American physicist: quoted, 26; experiments re ether-drag, 30, 40, 42, 48, 50
Miller, Dayton Clarence (1866-   ), American physicist: experiments of, 48
Millikan, Robert Andrews (1868-   ), American physicist: confirms Einstein's photo-electric equation, 88; experiments with radiations of very short wave length, 51; explains cosmic rays, 29
Minkowski (mǐn-kôf'skǐ), Herman (1864-1909), German mathematician, 43, 64
Molecule: quantum theory, 26
Momentum: Galileo's experiments, 19; Newton's laws, 20

Morley, Edward Williams (1838-1923), American chemist: experiments re ether-drag, 30, 40, 42, 48, 50

Motion: absolute and relative, 37; and velocity, 41; laws that govern, 42; Newton's laws, 20; velocity of, changes apparent length, 31

Motion, Accelerated, 19, 56, 58, 60*

Motion, Uniform: identical with rest, 56

Motion and rest, Relativity of, 9

Mutation: Einstein a, 13

Nature, Laws of, 42

Neptune: discovery of, 25

New York *Herald-Tribune*, 3, 5*, 84

Newton, Sir Isaac (1642-1727), English natural philosopher: contribution of, 20; his corpuscular theory of light, 29; laws of, applied to discovery of Neptune, 25; second law, 56

Newton's rings, 22

Optics: Newton's work, 22

Parallel lines, 63, 80, 82, 84

Past, present, and future: relativity of, 27, 45, 49

Pendulum timekeepers, 19

Perihelion (pĕr″ĭ-hē′lĭ-ŏn): of Mercury, 25, 71, 72*

Photo-electricity: Einstein's contribution, 6, 26, 88

Planck (plängk), Max (1858-   ), German physicist: quantum theory, 25

Plane, Bomb dropped from, 41

Planets, Motions of: Laplace-Lagrange controversy, 25

Potential energy, 47

Present, future, and past: relativity of, 27, 45, 49

Protagoras (prŏ-tăg′ŏ-răs) (481?-411 B.C.), Greek philosopher: teachings of, 16

Quantum Theory, 25

Radioactivity: and age of sun, 51; effect on first law of thermodynamics, 28

Radium: experiments of Rutherford and Soddy, 29; velocity of beta particle, 32

Reference body, has particular time, 44

Refraction, 29, 61

Relativity: corrections do not affect everyday matters, 53; general theory of, 55; historical background, 15; of direction, 7; of earth time, 11; of measurement, 17; of past, present, and future, 27, 45, 49; of rest and motion, 9; of time, 23, 48; of time and distance, 45; special theory of, 35

Rest: identical with uniform motion, 56; Newton's laws, 20

Rest and motion: relativity of, 9

Rest energy, 47

Riemann (rē′män), Georg Friedrich Bernard (1826-1866), German mathematician: geometry of, 83

River, You cannot step into the same, 15, 37

Robots: invention aided by Einstein, 8

Rumford (rŭm′fẽrd), Benjamin Thompson, Count (1753-1814), an American scientist: theory of conservation of energy, 22

Rutherford (rŭth′ẽr-fẽrd), Sir Ernest (1871-   ), British physicist: notices cosmic rays, 52; radium experiments, 28

Saturn: Laplace-Lagrange controversy, 25; orbit calculated by Kepler, 18

Second Law of Thermodynamics, 28

Soddy, Frederick (1877-   ), British physicist: radium experiments, 29

Space: and time, 43; infinite though bounded, 81; location in, 23; properties of, 61; unbounded though finite, 79; warping of, 70

Space-intervals, Moving, 46

Special theory of relativity, 35

Spectra of stars, 71

Spectrum: used to study electronic energy, 50

Spherical surface measurements, 62, 63

Sport: Einstein a, 13

Stars: number finite, 67

Steinmetz (stīn′mĕts), Charles Proteus (1865-1923), German-American electrician: calculates size of universe, 67; quoted, 47

Step twice into the same river, You cannot, 15, 37

Sun: deflection of rays passing, 61, 71, 73*, 74*; long life of, 29, 51

Telescope, Largest: range of, 70

Thermodynamics: discovery of radioactivity, 28; first law, 24; second law, 28

Thomson (tŏm′sŭn), Sir Joseph John (1856-   ), English physicist, 25

Time: apparent slowing up of, 65; as a co-ordinate, 43; location in, 23; relativity of, 11, 23, 45, 49

Timekeepers, 19

Triangle, Spherical, 63*, 82

Uniform-field equations, 83

Universe: finite or infinite, 66; size, 67

Uranus (ū′rà-nŭs): Laplace-Lagrange controversy, 25

Velocity: and motion, 41; changes apparent length, 31; changes mass, 31, 32*, 47; cross-stream, 39; highest of a material particle, 32; of light in a vacuum, 42; of wind and man, 38, 39

Velocity contraction theory, 31, 40, 46, 62

Venus: orbit calculated by Kepler, 18

Weight: Newton's law, 22

Work, Mechanical: relation to heat, 24

You can not step twice into the same river, 15, 37

Zeeman (zā'män), Pieter (1865-   ), Dutch physicist: experiments of, 48

Key to Pronunciation

ā as in dāy

â " " senâte

ă " " ădd

â " " câre

ä " " fär

à " " làst

ē as in mēte

ê " " êvent

ĕ " " ĕnd

ē " " tērm

ġ = j (gentile)

ḡ as in get

ī as in tīme

î " " îdea

ĭ " " ĭll

ī " " fīrm

ō " " ōld

ô " " ôbey

ŏ as in nŏt

ô " " lôrd

ū " " ūse

û " " ûnite

ŭ " " ŭs

û " " tûrn